W9-DGI-032

FOUNDATIONS OF MODERN PSYCHOLOGY SERIES
Richard S. Lazarus, *Editor*

CONRAD G. MUELLER

Professor of Psychology and Chairman of the Department of Psychology at Columbia University; researcher and author on the psychology and physiology of sensation.

Sensory

Psychology

PRENTICE-HALL, INC., *Englewood Cliffs, New Jersey*

© *Copyright 1965 by*
PRENTICE-HALL, INC.,
Englewood Cliffs, N. J.

All rights reserved. No part
of this book may be re-
produced in any form, by
mimeograph or any other
means, without permission
in writing from the pub-
lisher. Printed in the
United States of America.
Library of Congress Cata-
log Card No.: 65–13814.

SENSORY PSYCHOLOGY, *Conrad G. Mueller*

Second printing.....October, 1965

PRENTICE-HALL FOUNDATIONS
OF MODERN PSYCHOLOGY SERIES

Richard S. Lazarus, *Editor*

PRENTICE-HALL INTERNATIONAL, INC., *London*
PRENTICE-HALL OF AUSTRALIA, PTY., LTD., *Sydney*
PRENTICE-HALL OF CANADA, LTD., *Toronto*
PRENTICE-HALL OF INDIA PRIVATE LIMITED, *New Delhi*
PRENTICE-HALL OF JAPAN, INC., *Tokyo*

Designed by Harry Rinehart
Illustrated by Lorelle Raboni

C-80665 (p), C-80667 (c)

Foundations
of Modern Psychology
Series

The tremendous growth and vitality of psychology and its increasing fusion with the social and biological sciences demand a new approach to teaching at the introductory level. The basic course, geared as it usually is to a single text that tries to skim everything—that sacrifices depth for superficial breadth—is no longer adequate. Psychology has become too diverse for any one man, or a few men, to write about with complete authority. The alternative, a book that ignores many essential areas in order to present more comprehensively and effectively a particular aspect or view of psychology, is also insufficient. For in this solution, many key areas are simply not communicated to the student at all.

The Foundations of Modern Psychology is a new and different approach to the introductory course. The instructor is offered a series of short volumes, each a self-contained book on the special issues, methods, and content of a basic topic by a noted authority who is actively contributing to that particular field. And taken together, the volumes cover the full scope of psychological thought, research, and application.

The result is a series that offers the advantage of tremendous flexibility and scope. The teacher can choose the subjects he wants to emphasize and present them in the order he desires. And without necessarily sacrificing breadth, he can provide the student with a much fuller treatment of individual areas at the introductory level than is normally possible. If he does not have time to include all the volumes in his course, he can recommend the omitted ones as outside reading, thus covering the full range of psychological topics.

Psychologists are becoming increasingly aware of the importance of reaching the introductory student with high-quality, well-written, and stimulating material, material that highlights the continuing and exciting search for new knowledge. The Foundations of Modern Psychology Series is our attempt to place in the hands of instructors the best textbook tools for this purpose.

105571

Contents

Contents

vii

Introduction   This is a book about
sensory psychology, or the psychology of the senses.
Labels such as these do not lend themselves easily to
explicit definition. They have acquired a variety of
meanings through a long history of philosophy, experimental work, and theorizing about the subject matter.
Although it is not possible to define sensory psychology
exactly, still, this label denotes, in a rough way, a
topic within psychology that is of importance and that
poses many problems.

Our senses are sometimes referred to as our "avenues to the world." Although this statement does not tell us much about the senses, it does remind us that the only way we have of responding to the outside world is on the basis of information received, and operated on, by our sensory systems. This fact puts sensory psychology in a unique place in the history of science. As man began to formulate laws about the physical events he could observe, it was natural that he would begin to worry about how he knows what goes on in the world. We see evidence of this concern when we probe into the history of sensory psychology, for we find there the names of many scientists typically associated with the subject of physics. In the field of vision, for example, we encounter such names as Thomas Young, Clerk Maxwell, Isaac Newton, and Ernest Mach. Thomas Young is known to the physicists for his statement of the principle of interference, which provided the impetus for reviving Huygen's wave theory of light; he is known to the sensory psychologist for laying the foundation for a three-component theory of color vision. Clerk Maxwell made many contributions to molecular theory and to the electromagnetic theory of radiation, yet he wrote many papers on color vision; he devised one of the early schematic representations of color stimuli. The laws of motion and the techniques of the calculus are among Newton's many contributions, but he also wrote extensively in the area of color vision. Ernest Mach, who is well known for his classic work on mechanics, also wrote a book entitled *The Analysis of Sensation* and made many contributions to the study of contrast phenomena in vision.

It was not easy for early scientists to separate the disciplines we now call physics and sensory psychology; it was the things man saw that first set the problems of optics, it was the things man heard that first set the problems for acoustics. Only with an appropriate historical perspective can we appreciate man's early struggles to organize the data of both physics and sensory psychology. For example, the notion that objects radiate something that affects the eye was not easy to accept. The prevalent view in ancient times was that man saw things by having the mind send out some psychic "stuff" that came into contact with the thing seen. This view was called the "emanation hypothesis." There were some dissenters among scholars of that day, but this view was generally accepted and was propagated by the Arabic writers during the Dark Ages. This interpretation was sufficiently convincing for the early anatomists to believe that the optic nerve was hollow and served as the tube in which this psychic "stuff" was transmitted. In attempting to understand the prevalance of this view, it is possible to adopt any one of several positions. For example, we could say that it was difficult to determine exactly how the eye worked because scientists did not have a clear notion of what light was, or we could argue that it was difficult to figure out what light was because they did not know how the eye worked. However, the adoption of either position to the exclusion of the other would fail to do justice to the nature of human thought and the nature of the evolution of science. These two problems had to be worked on together until we could achieve an understanding that would permit us to separate two scientific areas of inquiry.

Another notion about the nature of seeing, one which persisted into the Renaissance period, was that the active region of the eye for sensing was the lens, rather than the retina. The reason for the persistence of this idea is of some interest. On the basis of what was known about the nature of light and the manner in which light was affected by materials such as glass and water, scientists felt that light coming into the eye would be imaged upside down on the retina. This possibility posed a serious problem for most scientists; it was difficult for them to accept the notion that the retina was the important structure for viewing because we do not see things as being upside down. There are many examples in the early drawings of Leonardo da Vinci that represent attempts to explain how the image might be made erect on the retina. Such attempts were destined to fail; it took a man of the stature and background of Kepler to present this problem in perspective. The first firm outline of the optics of the eye as we understand it today was presented by Kepler in 1604 in his book *Physiological Optics*. His account, of course, showed the image as being upside down on the retina. Subsequent knowledge and theory about physiological mechanisms in vision clearly demonstrated that the problem of image inversion that concerned many of the early investigators was not really a problem. However, this insight does not alter the historical fact that a concern over this question seriously influenced thought about the visual process for many years.

These are just two examples of a large list of notions that one encounters in the history of research and thought about sensory systems. They are offered here to suggest that we maintain an appropriate humility with respect to the ultimate correctness of the views and assumptions which we now employ in talking about sensory functioning and which we frequently accept as being obvious, self-evident, and unmodifiable.

As man's understanding of physical phenomena progressed, it became obvious that the continued advance in the physical sciences was not to be limited to those aspects of the world for which man possessed specialized receptors. With the gradual accumulation of data and the development of physical theory, it became possible to design measuring instruments that could free the physical sciences from a dependence on a particular sense modality. Further, it became possible to define certain physical dimensions in terms that were independent of any specific sensory system; these dimensions became dependent, instead, on an understanding of the physics of the measuring instrument. I do not mean to imply that the physical scientist did, or indeed ever can, completely free himself from a dependence on the human observer at some stage of the measuring process. The point to be emphasized is that it did become possible, in principle, to measure light without using the eye, to measure acoustic waves without using the ear, and to extend the range of study of physical energy changes.

With the emergence of a physical science that no longer depended on the unique ways in which humans responded to the environment, several new lines of inquiry were made available to us. We could now study the relations between these newly defined physical events and the response of the human observer to them. In a very crude way these relations define the subject matter of sensory psychology. A second line of inquiry also developed in man's quest for an understanding of how information about the environment is acquired. This second area of study was directed toward the question of how our sensory equipment accomplishes the transformation of physical energy into a form that is useful to the sensing organism. In equally crude terms these relations define the subject matter of sensory physiology. From a strictly logical point of view nothing in the nature of these two subject matters demands that they be explored jointly. In point of fact, however, these two fields have developed together. Each has contributed to the other, either in posing problems for study or in offering interpretations of results obtained. Behavioral experiments have been done because of some available evidence regarding the nature of the sensing mechanism. Physiological experiments have been performed because of known facts about the way in which living organisms respond to stimuli.

Not only has there been a cross-fertilization between the disciplines of sensory psychology and sensory physiology, but individual research workers have also crossed these arbitrary boundaries in an attempt to understand what our sensory capacities are and what makes them what they are. Physicists and physiologists have made important contributions to the behavioral data; psychologists have made important contributions to the physiology of sensory systems. This is a fact about scientific inquiry that we cannot ignore. For example, one of the important steps in the history of electrophysiology of the auditory system was an experiment performed by two psychologists, Glenn Wever and Charles Bray; the first recording of electrical activity in single nerve fibers in the visual system was a joint effort of a biologist and a psychologist, H. K. Hartline and Clarence Graham; the recording of activity in single nerve fibers in the taste system was also the work of a psychologist, Carl Pfaffmann. Intellectual traffic in the opposite direction is also common. One of the most systematic and quantitative attacks on the problems of visual phychophysics in the 1930's came out of a laboratory of biophysics under the direction of Selig Hecht, a zoologist.

The interaction of the physiological and psychological studies of sensory processes has been quite fruitful in the past, and, at this stage in history, it is hardly appropriate to review either one without some discussion of the other. The primary emphasis in this volume will be on the behavioral data of sensory psychology. By this I mean that behavioral studies will guide us to the problems that will be discussed. Nevertheless, we shall use both types of research to help elucidate the problems and the existing solutions.

SOME EXPERIMENTAL METHODS

In the remaining chapters we shall attempt to look at some of the specific ways in which we respond to various stimuli. Before doing this, however, we might ask ourselves one simple question. How do we go about studying what an organism can see or hear? For example, how can we tell whether a human subject sees a light stimulus? Our first answer is likely to be, "Ask him." If we present a light of very weak intensity to a subject, he is likely to say that he does not see it; if we present a light of high intensity, the subject is likely to say that he does see it. The important thing to note about such observations is that the subject responds differently in the presence of two different stimuli. He gives one response to small amounts of light or no light; he gives another response to a bright light. At this stage of analysis we need not be concerned with the specific responses that are used. Whether the subject has been trained to speak English or French or Russian does not change the nature of the problem. In fact, we may, for convenience, use responses not involving the spoken word; we may have the subject press one key if he sees the light and press another key if he does not. It is the fact that the subject behaves lawfully that makes the problem tractable.

A full appreciation of this apparently trivial point turns out to be of utmost importance. If we can remember it we shall achieve two things. First of all, we shall keep our perspective with respect to the use of the spoken word in psychophysical experiments. For example, the fact that we associate certain words such as "red," "orange," "yellow," "green," and "blue" with different regions of the spectrum, while some other culture does not, tells us little about the relative capacities to see colors. In such a case the question should not be whether a person *does* discriminate different colors; the question is whether he *can*. Obviously, if he does discriminate the differences, then we say he can; but if a person does not discriminate different parts of the spectrum, only appropriate training can tell us whether he can. This point will be obvious if you think of extreme cases. Most of us would agree, for instance, that a person who is mute could have normal vision, yet he will never utter the sounds "I see it" or "That is red." Similarly, we may encounter individuals classified as hysterically blind; their visual systems are functioning normally, as shown by the use of visual stimuli as conditioned stimuli in training, yet they will say that they do not see visual stimuli.

The second thing we achieve by this emphasis on differential responding to different stimuli is that it permits us to make the transition from the sensory performance of man to that in lower organisms. We can thus make comparisons of sensory capacity in different species and place the data of sensory psychology in a comparative setting.

One of the most common measurements used in sensory psychology is called the threshold. The notion of a threshold is one that is readily accepted by most of us. We would all agree that there are lights so dim that we cannot see them, other lights that are bright enough so that we can see them. The simplest definition of a threshold is that it is a point, or a region, on an intensity scale below which we do not detect the stimulus and above which we do. That thresholds exist is intuitively obvious. Intuition does not tell us what difficulties may arise if we try to measure the threshold exactly.

Our first approach to threshold measurement might be to explore for it systematically. We could begin with a stimulus that cannot be detected and gradually increase the intensity until the stimulus is detected. Alternatively, we could start with an intensity that is easily detected and gradually decrease the intensity until the stimulus is no longer detected. In essence, this is one of the methods that is used in studying thresholds. It is called *the method of limits*. In practice, the method presents a number of problems. The thresholds we obtain depend on a number of subtle features of the test situation. The threshold will be influenced by the size of the steps we take as we change intensity or by the rate of change of the stimulus if we adjust the intensity continuously. It is also usually true that we obtain different thresholds from ascending and descending runs. However, the thing that is likely to disturb an experimenter the most is that a subject may shift his response several times. The subject may start out saying that he does not see the light if we begin the search with weak stimulus intensities. We will eventually reach an intensity to which he will respond, "Yes, I see it," but if we present the next higher step in intensity he may respond again with "No, I don't see it." The likelihood of encountering this reversal will depend on the size of the intensity step, but it is not an infrequent occurrence. It suggests an important property of threshold measurements: Responding near threshold is a probabilistic matter.

The fact that there is some uncertainty in the response at threshold suggests another method of measuring the threshold. With this procedure the first step is to find the approximate region in which the response uncertainty exists; the next step is to select a series of stimuli that will cover the range from a point where the subject will rarely detect the stimulus to a point where he will always detect it; the final step is to present these chosen stimuli in random order many times and measure the relative frequency of occurrence of detections. The method just outlined is called *the method of constant stimuli*. If we plot the obtained detection frequencies as a function of the stimulus intensity, we obtain what is called a psychometric function. An example of such a function is shown in Figure I.

Our primary concern in subsequent chapters will not be with the question of which psychophysical method was used or with the detailed shape of the psychometric function. We shall be interested in how the average threshold obtained from the method of limits or how the 50 per cent point of the psychometric function will change from one experimental condition to another. When we say that the visual threshold depends on the color of the stimulus or that the hearing threshold depends on age, we shall mean that a curve, such as that shown in Figure I, shifts with the color of the stimulus or the age of the subject. If we show a graph to illustrate such statements, we shall be plotting how the 50 per cent point of the psychometric function, say, varies with the color of the stimulus. Problems centering on the psychophysical methods *per se* will not, however, be our primary concern.

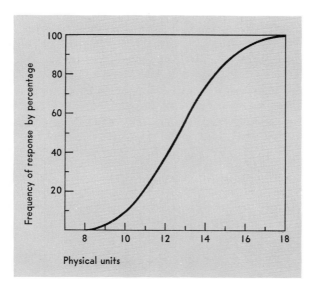

Figure I. Typical psychophysical function showing the frequency of response as a function of stimulus intensity.

Vision   One of the most impor-
tant problems in sensory psychology is the specification
of the stimuli we study. Visual stimuli come from a
narrow band in the electromagnetic spectrum, a band
that covers wavelengths of radiation ranging approximately from 400 millimicrons to 700 millimicrons. These
words require a little explanation. We usually describe
visual stimuli in one of two ways. One way, based on the
conception that light is propagated in a wave-like manner, describes light in terms of wavelength and frequency.
According to another conception, light is radiated in the
form of discrete particles called quanta. The subtleties in

7

1

physical theory that permit us to unify these apparently quite disparate views need not concern us. When we say that a person with normal vision is sensitive to light in the range from 400 to 700 millimicrons we simply mean that these stimuli have wavelengths in that range. A millimicron is one thousandth of a millionth of a meter or one millionth of a millimeter.

We shall start our discussion of vision by examining some of the factors influencing our absolute sensitivity to radiant energy. Then we shall turn our attention to other types of sensitivity, particularly our sensitivity to intensity differences and to the spatial and temporal distribution of light. Thirdly, we shall examine some of the data bearing on color vision and, finally, we shall consider some special perceptual problems.

Spectral Sensitivity

We are not equally sensitive to all portions of the band of electromagnetic stimuli. If we measure the minimum energy required by a human observer to see a stimulus from the visible spectrum, we find that we are about 1000 times more sensitive in the middle of this band than we are at the extremes. An example of the results obtained from a quantitative determination of these thresholds at various parts of the spectrum is shown in Figure 1-1. This figure tells us several important things about human vision. First, it shows us the exact way in which the threshold depends on the wavelength of the stimulus. Second, it shows that there are at least two such functions. It suggests that we have

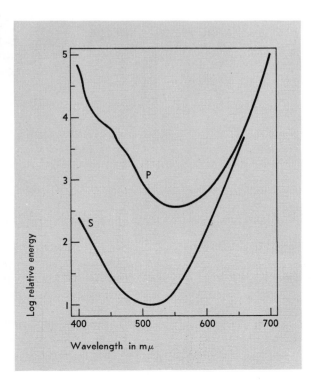

Figure 1-1. Absolute visual thresholds, in relative energy units, as a function of the wavelength of the stimulus. S—scotopic curve; P—photopic curve. (F.A. Geldard. The human senses. New York: Wiley, 1953.)

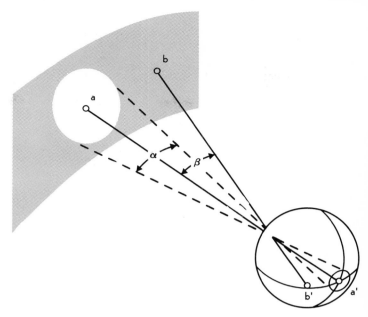

Figure 1-2. Schematic representation of visual angle measurements.

two visual systems. We can understand the importance of these measurements if we examine in more detail exactly how we do such experiments on visual sensitivity. Curve *P* in Figure 1-1 can be most easily obtained by using a small visual test stimulus and presenting it along the direct line of sight of the eye. Consider the schematic representation of the eye in Figure 1-2. If we instruct the subject to fixate on the center of the ring and present the test stimulus in the center of this fixation ring, the stimulus *a* will be imaged at *a'* and we will be measuring the sensitivity of this region. If the threshold is measured as a function of wavelength under these conditions, Curve *P* in Figure 1-1 will be obtained. This is called the photopic curve. On the other hand, if we instruct our subject to fixate at *a* but we present the test stimulus at *b*, this stimulus will be imagined at *b'* and we then obtain Curve *S* of Figure 1-1. This is called the scotopic curve.

It is important to remember that Figure 1-1 represents the *thresholds* for different wavelengths of the test stimulus. Another way of representing these data is to plot *sensitivity* as a function of wavelength. Sensitivity is defined as the reciprocal of the absolute threshold; therefore, the lower the threshold, the higher the sensitivity. If we take the reciprocals of the thresholds shown in Figure 1-1 and call the maximum sensitivity for each curve 100 per cent, then the two curves in Figure 1-1 assume the form shown in Figure 1-3. These are called visibility curves.

White light is usually made up of a mixture of all the visible wavelengths, although it can be demonstrated that mixtures of a very small number of wavelengths will appear white to the normal human observer. Whenever we measure the threshold for white light we are measuring some kind of average threshold for components whose thresholds are plotted in Figure 1-1.

The photopic visibility curve, Curve *P* in Figure 1-3, becomes important when we attempt to measure stimulus intensity. Measures of the intensity of

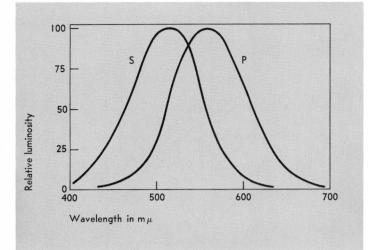

Figure 1-3. Visibility curves. Relative visibility as a function of the wavelength of the stimulus. S—scotopic curve; P—photopic curve. (S. Hecht and W.E. Williams. J. gen. Physiol., 1922, 5, 1–34.)

visual stimuli offer us a choice of two major classes of units. The units of one set are called *radiometric units*. When we use these units we measure the radiant energy provided by the stimulus. The important feature of the units in this class is that they directly represent the energy characteristics of the stimulus. The units of the second set are called *luminous energy units*. When we use these measures we begin with the measurement of the radiant energy of the stimulus, but we correct, or adjust, these measurements in terms of the effectiveness of the radiant energy for the human eye. We use the visibility curve shown in Curve *P* of Figure 1-3 to do this. In other words, we multiply the radiant energy at each wavelength by its effectiveness as given by Curve *P*. Such measurements yield the dimensions of luminous energy. If our apparatus uses a projection bulb as a light source it is likely to radiate a considerable amount of energy in the infrared region. This portion of the energy is ineffective because the eye is not very sensitive in this region of the spectrum. Luminous units correct for this fact. Two light sources that emit the same amount of radiant energy may or may not emit the same amount of luminous energy; whether they do will depend on whether they emit comparable amounts of energy in the regions of the spectrum we are sensitive to.

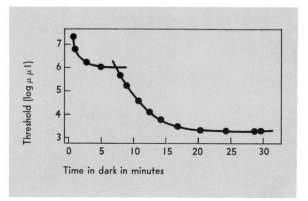

Figure 1-4. Dark-adaptation curve. Absolute threshold for a visual stimulus as a function of time in the dark. (S. Hecht. In C. Murchison (ed.). Handbook of general experimental psychology. Worcester: Clark Univ. Press, 1934.)

Our ability to detect visual stimuli depends on a large number of conditions. One of the most important of these is the state of adaptation of the subject. We are all familiar with the fact that when we go from a highly illuminated environment to one of dim illumination—for example, from afternoon brightness to the illumination of a movie theater—our ability to see objects is very poor. A similar problem is encountered if we go from a very dimly illuminated environment to one of high light-intensity. It is also a common observation that the longer we remain in a given illuminated environment the better we can resolve the visual details. The gradual accommodation to a new level of illumination is called adaptation.

One of the simplest ways of measuring the course of adaptation quantitatively is to expose a subject to a known stimulus intensity for a fixed period of time, reduce this intensity to zero, and then present test stimuli to measure how the absolute threshold varies with the time in the dark. An example of the experimental results obtained in such an experiment is shown in Figure 1-4. This curve of dark-adaptation drops rapidly at first and then more and more slowly, finally levelling off at a value that is characteristic of the dark-adaptation threshold for the particular stimulus used. It is important to note the magnitude of the threshold change. In this experiment the threshold at the beginning of dark-adaptation is about 10,000 times higher than the threshold after 30 minutes in the dark.

Both the magnitude and the shape of the dark-adaptation curve depend on a number of features of the experimental procedure. These features fall into two broad classes, the characteristics of the adaptation conditions and the characteristics of the test stimulus.

We can illustrate the effect of the first class of conditions by showing the effect of the intensity of the adapting stimulus to which the subject is exposed before we begin to measure dark-adaptation. The results from one experiment are shown in Figure 1-5. In general, we may summarize these results by saying that the greater the amount of prior light-adaptation the longer it takes to dark-adapt. Similar effects are observed if the duration of the light-adapting stimulus is varied. The longer the duration of the adapting light, the slower is dark-adaptation and the longer it takes to reach the final threshold. Our sensitivity recovers very rapidly from an exposure to a flash of a photographic flashgun even though the brightness is great; our sensitivity will recover more slowly from several hours of daylight illumination even though the intensity at any given moment is less than we receive from the brief flash of a photographic flashgun.

It is, of course, not necessary to study the adaptation process by investigating only our adjustment to complete darkness. We obtain the same kinds of results if we measure our adjustment to dim illumination; the only major difference is the final level to which the threshold drops. We can represent the general case schematically in Figure 1-6. If we are adapted to one level and then study the manner in which we gradually adjust to another level, the changes in threshold would be as depicted in this figure. Included in this figure are two examples of adaptation to a higher intensity level; these represent cases of what is called light-adaptation. This figure shows us that the

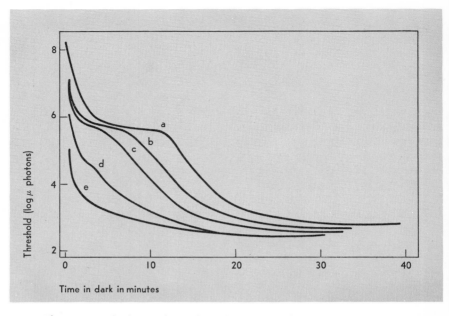

Figure 1-5. Series of dark-adaptation curves. Curves a through e represent decreasing intensities of previous light-adaptation. (S. Hecht, C. Haig, and A.M. Chase. J. gen. Physiol., 1934, 20, 831–850.)

changes in threshold during adaptation may increase as well as decrease. If we are measuring the process of adaptation to a light that is dimmer than the pre-adapting stimulus (dark-adaptation), the threshold decreases; if we are measuring the process of adaptation to a light that is brighter than the pre-adapting stimulus (light-adaptation), the threshold increases.

The use of the labels light- and dark-adaptation is somewhat arbitrary. In

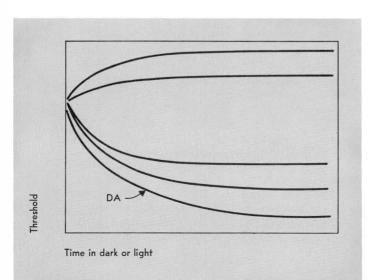

Figure 1-6. Schematic representation of a series of light- and dark-adaptation curves. The different curves are obtained by allowing the eye to adapt to different levels of intensity. The lowest curve, DA, represents adaptation to complete darkness.

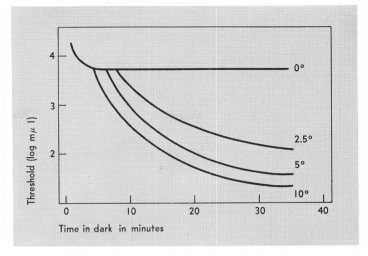

Figure 1-7. Series of dark-adaptation curves obtained at different retinal positions. The number on each curve represents the distance, in angular units, that the test stimulus was from the fixation point. (S. Hecht, C. Haig, and G. Wald. J. gen. Physiol., 1934, 19, 321–337.)

a sense, all the curves in Figure 1-6, except the lowest one, represent adaptation to light. It is customary, however, to speak of light-adaptation only in those cases of change to a higher level of intensity; any adjustment to a lower level is referred to as dark- or dim-adaptation. This custom is not completely arbitrary, however; the time course of these two processes is different. Light-adaptation seems to be much more rapid.

The second class of conditions that influence dark-adaptation involves the specific characteristics of the test stimulus. One of the most important examples in this category is the effect of the position of the test stimulus in the visual field. We can anticipate these results by remembering that the two curves of Figure 1-1 were obtained by testing at two different positions in the visual field. In that figure, we found that the thresholds in the periphery were lower than those for central vision except for wavelengths in the red end of the spectrum. When we measure the course of dark-adaptation at different positions in the visual field we observe the expected result; the threshold change during adaptation is greater in the periphery than it is in the visual field. A typical result is shown in Figure 1-7, where the number on each curve indicates the number of degrees of visual angle the center of the stimulus is away from the line of sight of the eye. This angle is shown schematically as angle β in Figure 1-2.

The effect of position in the visual field can be shown more clearly if the subject is first completely dark-adapted and we then measure absolute threshold for different positions of the stimulus. This is equivalent to cutting across a whole family of curves of the sort shown in Figure 1-7, at a point where the curves are no longer dropping. We can then plot these terminal thresholds as a function of the position of the stimulus in the visual field. When we actually determine these points experimentally, we obtain the results shown in Figure 1-8. One of the surprising features of this figure is that it shows that the center of the eye is one of the most insensitive regions. This is a fact of great importance in training for military night-lookout duties or other such activities. If a potential stimulus is very near threshold, we have a greater likelihood of detecting it if we do not look directly at the region where it is to appear. We are about ten times more sensitive in a

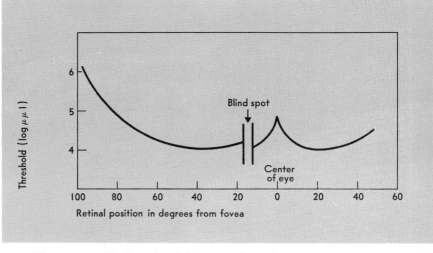

Figure 1-8. Absolute threshold of the dark-adapted eye as a function of the retinal position of the stimulus. A blind spot exists where the optic nerve leaves the eye. (Modified from L. Sloan. Amer. J. Ophthal., 1947, 30, 705–720.)

region that is about 20 degrees to the side of our fixation point than we are at the point of fixation.

The Importance of the Size and Duration of the Stimulus

Two other important properties of the test stimulus that will influence the value of the absolute threshold are its size and the duration of its exposure. One general rule that seems to hold for small test stimuli of short duration is that the product of the area, the intensity, and the exposure time must reach some critical value if the stimulus is to be detected. This rule means that if we decrease the exposure time by a factor of two, we must increase the intensity or the area by a factor of two in order to have the stimulus detected.

The reciprocal relation between the exposure time and the intensity of the stimulus is called the Bunsen-Roscoe law. The law is borrowed from the field of photochemistry, where it has been shown that the product of the intensity and the exposure time must be a constant to produce a constant photochemical effect (such as a fixed density in a photographic negative). This accords with the experience of photographers; if one wishes to decrease the exposure time (in order, say, to stop movement), one has to open the diaphragm (decrease the *f* number) to let in more light by a proportionate amount. This empirical generalization seems to hold for human vision for exposure times up to about one-twentieth of a second. The reciprocal relation between area of the stimulus and threshold intensity, known as Ricco's law, holds for stimuli smaller than 20 or 30 minutes of visual angle.

It is important to emphasize that these generalizations hold only over limited ranges of exposure time and size. Over the full range of size and duration the relations are much more complicated. For example, the Bunsen-

Roscoe law holds for short exposure times; for long exposure times the duration is irrelevant. For small areas, this shift from one rule to the other is very sharp as is shown in Figure 1-9. This figure shows the amount of energy required at threshold as a function of the duration of the stimulus. Let us examine this graph in more detail. Each data point in this figure was obtained by fixing the exposure time at some value and adjusting the intensity of the light flash until the subject could just see it. This procedure is repeated, selecting another exposure time and again adjusting the intensity until the subject could just detect the stimulus. The energy of each test flash is computed by multiplying the intensity by the duration of the flash. If we require a fixed amount of energy to get a threshold effect, as would be expected if the Bunsen-Roscoe law applies to vision, all of the data points should fall on a straight line of zero slope. This seems to be the case for durations up to approximately one tenth of a second. Beyond this point the observations seem to fall along a straight line having a slope of one. This slope of one signifies that in this range we must deliver a fixed intensity in order to reach threshold. The slope is one because, if the value of intensity is a constant at threshold, we are actually plotting the logarithm of the duration against itself. The transition from a horizontal line to a line with a slope of one becomes increasingly gradual as we increase the size of the test stimulus. The dashed line in Figure 1-9 shows results obtained with a large stimulus.

Intensity Discrimination

Most of the visual stimuli we encounter in everyday experience are seen against a background that is also visible. In the simplest case we have a stimulus figure of one brightness and a background of another brightness. When we measure threshold

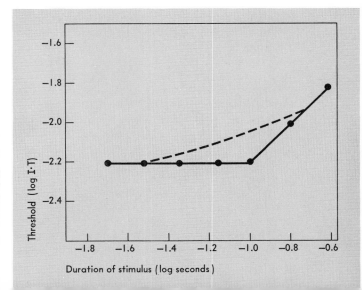

Figure 1-9. Threshold energy as a function of the duration of a visual stimulus. (Modified from G.E. Long. J. opt. Soc. Amer., 1951, 41, 743–747.)

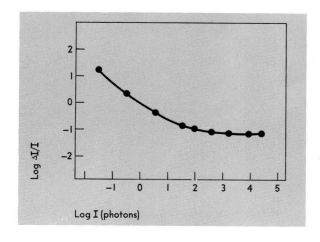

Figure 1-10. Differential threshold as a function of the intensity of the background stimulus. (C.G. Mueller. J. gen. Physiol., 1951, 34, 463.)

differences between these two intensities we are studying intensity discrimination. In a sense, we can view the absolute threshold measurement as a special case of intensity discrimination, the background intensity being zero.

The measurement of our capacity to discriminate one level of intensity from another is a classical experiment in psychophysics. In fact, many theories of sensory experience took as their point of departure the data on intensity discrimination, the so-called just noticeable difference, or jnd. Since it is possible to think of the absolute threshold as a special case of intensity discrimination, it is not surprising that most of the conditions that influence absolute threshold also influence the difference threshold. For example, the area of the stimulus and the duration of the exposure have the same effect on the difference threshold as on the absolute threshold. There is one factor, however, that cannot be studied in both kinds of experiments—the intensity of the background. As we increase the intensity of the background on which an increment in intensity is placed we find that the magnitude of the increment in intensity that is necessary in order to reach threshold gradually increases. One of the early descriptions of how this increment threshold changes with the level of the background is found in what is called the Weber-Fechner law. This law states that the increment threshold changes with the background intensity in such a way that the ratio of increment (ΔI) to the background intensity (I) is always a constant. It is now known that this law holds only over limited ranges of background intensity. If we study a large range of values of the background intensity, we observe that this ratio changes as is shown in Figure 1-10. There we see that this ratio is large at very low background level. At the high intensity levels the curve is approximately flat; this is the region over which the Weber-Fechner law holds.

SPATIAL AND TEMPORAL RESOLUTION

Visual Acuity

In the preceding parts of this chapter we have been concerned with measuring sensitivity by adjusting the intensity of the stimulus figure until it is just visible a certain percentage of the time. There are other experimental procedures for determining thresholds. Suppose we present the subject with a large uniformly lighted field containing a thin vertical black line. Let us make the background illumination bright enough so that the subject always sees the circular field, and let us adjust the thickness of the black line so that it is just visible. In other words, we are determining a "thickness" threshold; we are measuring some capacity to resolve detail. This is one of the simplest measures of what is called *visual acuity*. The size of the line that will just be detectable is dependent on the brightness of the background against which it is presented. The threshold width will be large for very dim illuminations, small at high levels of illumination. Against a background having the brightness of a clear daylight sky we are able to resolve a line subtending no more than half a second of visual angle. This is roughly equivalent to a fine wire, .01 inch in diameter, seen at 100 yards. For us to achieve this degree of resolution, however, the line must be very long. As we shorten the length of the line we have to make it wider and wider in order to see it. If we measured the threshold of a long wire against the sky at dusk we would also find that it had to be many times thicker. There is a clear quantitative relation between the fineness of a line that can just be detected and the brightness of the background against which we view it. This relation is shown in Figure 1-11.

The kind of visual acuity just described is called *minimum visible acuity*. There is another kind of measurement of our ability to resolve detail that is called *minimum separable acuity*. Measurements of this kind of acuity usually involve some type of repetitive pattern, such as the line grating in Figure 1-12. Another example of this second type of acuity figure is the checkerboard pattern, also shown in Figure 1-12. If we use a line grating pattern in which the dark and light spaces are of equal width, we find that acuity is again dependent on the brightness of the visual field, but the maximum resolution possible for the normal observer is approximately 30 seconds of visual angle, instead of less than one second as for a single line.

In the discussion of the visibility of thin lines we deliberately used as an illustration a dark line on a bright background. There is an important reason for doing so; the only limit to our ability to detect fine bright lines, or small bright points, on a dark background is the intensity of the line or the point. This is clearly indicated by the visibility of the stars which, because of their great distances, subtend infinitesimally small visual angles. They are visible because of their tremendous light output.

We have said that the actual threshold visual angles we obtain when we measure minimum visible acuity and minimum separable acuity are not the same.

Figure 1-11. Threshold visual angle as a function of background stimulus intensity. (S. Hecht, E. Mintz. J. gen. Physiol., 1939, 22, 593–612.)

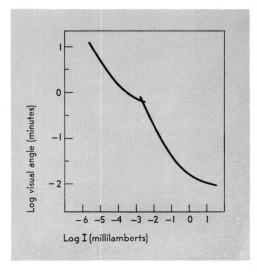

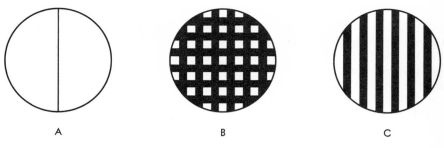

A   B   C

Figure 1-12. Types of acuity figures. (A) Minimum visible. (B) and (C) Minimum separable.

Nevertheless, these measures of visual acuity will usually increase and decrease in the same way as we change the test conditions. For example, the amount of detail we can see increases with increasing intensity, and it decreases as we move the test stimulus farther out in the periphery of the visual field.

Figure 1-13. Critical flicker frequency as a function of the intensity of the flickering light. The numbers on each curve represent the size of the flickering stimulus measured in degrees of visual angle. (S. Hecht and E.L. Smith. J. gen. Physiol., 1936, 19, 979–988.)

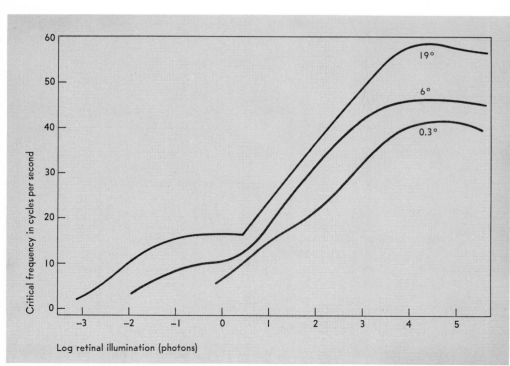

Another type of resolution
that is of both theoretical and practical importance in the study of vision is
called *temporal resolution*. To what extent can we separate stimuli that occur
at different points in time? When we study the capacity to detect the temporal alternation of a visual stimulus—that is, to detect a stimulus that is
repetitively changing from bright to dark and back to bright again—we are
studying flicker discrimination. The rate at which we are just able to see
an alternating light as flickering is called *the critical flicker frequency*.

We all know that at some rates of alternation we will see flickering lights
as steady. We do not usually see the 60-cycle ripple in our household lighting,
or the flicker in commercial movies; we are likely to see the flicker of home
movies because the rate of alternation is typically slower. Once again we find
that one of the most important variables influencing flicker discrimination
is the intensity of the alternating light. In fact, the eye is easily able to resolve the alternation rates used in commercial movies if the intensity is high
enough. These alternations are not normally seen because of the dim illumination of the movie screen. The exact relation between the critical flicker
frequency and the intensity of the alternating light is shown in Figure 1-13.
It is clear that temporal resolution is poor at very dim intensities and may be
as low as five or ten cycles per second. This temporal resolving power increases with increasing intensity and typically reaches a maximum around
50 or 60 cycles per second, although this maximum depends on the size of the
flickering area and on its location in the visual field. Our temporal resolution
is better for large areas than it is for small areas. Critical flicker frequencies
as high as 100 flashes per second have been obtained when the whole eye is
flooded with the flashing light.

COLOR VISION

Wavelength Discrimination

Let us return now to the
visibility of different portions of the visible spectrum and to our ability to
discriminate different parts of this spectrum. One important distinction
between the photopic and scotopic systems which yield, respectively, the *P*
and *S* curves in Figure 1-1, relates to color vision. Let us restrict ourselves,
for the moment, to the photopic system. Here we find not only that we have
different thresholds for different wavelengths, but also that once we increase
the intensity above the threshold value for two widely separated wavelengths
we can tell the difference between these two wavelengths on the basis of their
colored appearance. This is not true for the scotopic system.

It is natural to ask how far apart the wavelengths of two stimuli must be
in order to insure that a normal subject will be able to tell that the stimuli are
different in color or hue. This is a threshold measurement, but it is a threshold
for a difference in wavelength. Since the appearance of a difference in hue or
color is what the subject reports, we are studying wavelength discrimination
or hue discrimination. We can do this experiment in several ways. We can
pick several representative wavelengths spaced through the spectrum and

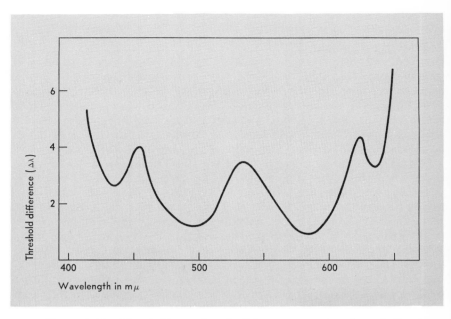

Figure 1-14. Threshold wavelength difference as a function of the wavelength of the comparison stimulus. (L.T. Troland. Psychophysiology, Vol. II: Sensation. *New York: Van Nostrand, 1930.)*

measure how much we have to change these wavelengths in order for a subject to report that there is a difference. A second technique is to start at one end of the spectrum and change the wavelength until the subject reports a difference in color, then use that second wavelength as a reference stimulus and move a just-detectable-distance farther along the wavelength dimension. This procedure is continued until we cover the visible spectrum. With both procedures we find that the size of the steps that we have to take, in order for the subject to detect a change, varies with the region of the spectrum in which we are working. A typical result from this second type of experiment is shown in Figure 1-14. This figure shows us a rather complicated function. Over most of the spectrum we are able to detect changes of the order of one to three millimicrons. From the results of this procedure it has been estimated that between 400 and 700 mμ there are over 120 discriminable steps.

Color Mixture

The most important data in the study of color vision come from the study of color mixtures. One of the most remarkable observations about color mixing is that it is possible to select three monochromatic stimuli in such a way that by simply adjusting their relative intensities, we are able to match any other color in the spectrum. When such experiments are done, the three wavelengths selected to make the match are called primary wavelengths. Three commonly used primaries are 460 (blue), 530 (green), and 650 (red) millimicrons, but many other combinations could be used. An example of the relative proportions of three pri-

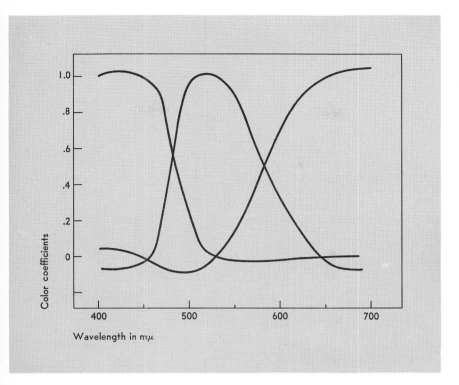

Figure 1-15. Trichromatic coefficients for various wavelengths of the stimulus to be matched. (C.H. Graham and Y. Hsia. Science, *1958, 127, 675.)*

maries that are required to match all the colors of the spectrum are shown in Figure 1-15. Note that one of the curves always has a negative value. It is important that we understand the meaning of these negative values, since it is certain that we do not wish to imply that we are literally using negative intensities. These values occur because the common interpretation of our statement about color mixture is not strictly true. It is possible to select any color in the spectrum and a set of three primaries and to achieve a color match by an adjustment in the intensities of the three primaries. It is not, however, always possible to mix the three primaries *together* and get them to match all of the colors in the spectrum. One of the primaries must be mixed with the to-be-matched color. In this sense the third primary is subtracted from the other two. The real match is between two pairs of colors. The primary that is mixed with the reference color is given a negative sign, following algebraic convention. Thus, the basic color-mixing equation would be

$$a \{\lambda_c\} + b \{\lambda_{p1}\} = c \{\lambda_{p2}\} + d \{\lambda_{p3}\}$$

This equation is read as follows: for any wavelength, λ_c, in the spectrum, it is possible to take an amount, a, of this wavelength plus an amount, b, of one of the primaries, λ_{p1}, and have the mixture of these two match the color of a mixture of the other two primaries whose intensities we adjust so that we have an amount, c, of λ_{p2} and an amount, d, of λ_{p3}. If we assume that we can manipulate these symbols in the same manner as terms in any algebraic expression, then we can solve for the term we are varying in the experiment, the comparison wavelength, λ_c. Since the primary wavelengths are constant throughout the color-mixture experiment, we place all of the primaries on one side of the equation. In changing one of the primaries from one side to the other we change its sign. We, therefore, obtain

$$a\ \{\lambda_c\} = c\ \{\lambda_{p2}\} + d\ \{\lambda_{p3}\} - b\ \{\lambda_{p1}\}$$

The fact that it is possible to achieve this kind of match using only three primaries suggests that we may have only three different color-receiving mechanisms. If this is true, it may, at first glance, seem surprising that our ability to detect wavelength differences is so well developed. For example, we may wonder how it is possible to detect wavelength differences of the order of three or four millimicrons over most of this visible spectrum if we have, as postulated by trichromatic theory, only three color receptors to cover the spectrum from 400 mμ to 700 mμ.

The easiest way to think about the linkage between the wavelength-discrimination data and the color-mixture data is to think in terms of a small number of receptor systems, each of which responds differently to variations in wavelength. It might be expected that, in regions of the spectrum where the responsiveness of these receptor systems was changing rapidly with wavelength, we ought to be able to detect small changes in wavelength. This idea can be made clearer by considering an extreme example. Suppose we had three receptor systems with the sensitivity curves shown in Figure 1-16A. The first response system gives no response for wavelengths shorter than 400 mμ. Between 400 mμ and 550 mμ it has a sensitivity of ten units; it gives no response for wavelengths longer than 550 mμ. The other curves are to be interpreted in the same way, except that the transition wavelengths are 450 mμ and 600 mμ for the second response system, and 500 mμ and 700 mμ for the third response system. The response patterns that we would obtain for all the wavelengths between 400 mμ and 700 mμ are shown in Figure 1-16B. With this set of sensitivity curves we would not be able to tell the difference between a stimulus of 400 mμ and one of 449 mμ but we could differ between a stimulus of 449 mμ and one having a wavelength of 450 mμ. We could not tell the difference between 450 mμ and 499 mμ but we could tell the difference between a wavelength of 499 mμ and 500 mμ. With these sensitivity curves we would obtain a wavelength discrimination function that would look like the curve shown in Figure 1-16B. We have deliberately selected these hypothetical rectangular sensitivity curves so that they would yield maxima and minima that look a little like those actually obtained with human observers. The point is that wavelength discrimination is good in those regions where the sensitivity curves are changing rapidly.

Undoubtedly the receptor systems actually operating in human vision do not have such sharp transitions, but the figure does illustrate why it is important to consider that the regions where sensitivity is changing rapidly are important in wavelength discrimination. In a region where there are big shifts in the relative amount of responding among receptors, the pattern of responding shifts significantly with small changes in wavelength and we say

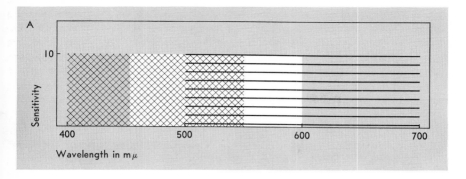

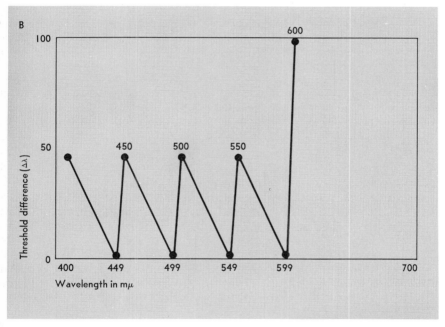

Figure 1-16. (A) Hypothetical sensitivity curves for three color receptors. (B) A wavelength discrimination function that might be obtained from the hypothetical sensitivity curves shown in (A).

that discrimination is good. The basis for this idea may be seen in the experimental data by noting that the two points in the spectrum showing the best wavelength discrimination—that is, the two deepest dips in the curve in Figure 1-14 (approximately 490 and 585 millimicrons)—correspond to the two regions where two of the curves in Figure 1-15 are changing most rapidly.

One special case of the mixture of colors is the case of complementary colors. There are many pairs of wavelengths in the spectrum whose mixture gives an achromatic or colorless appearance. Red (671 mµ) with blue-green (493 mµ) and yellow (580 mµ) with blue (478 mµ) are examples of such pairs. The notion that colors may be linked together in pairs, such as we find in the complementary colors, is encountered in a number of places in the study of color vision. For example, we find a similar kind of linkage in the study of simultaneous color contrast. If we look at a small grey stimulus with a brightly colored surround we see the center grey area as having a colored appearance approximately that of the complementary of the surround. A second place where we encounter this pairing of colors is in after-images. If we expose a subject to a brightly colored stimulus and then eliminate the stimulus, one of the prominent things the subject reports is seeing a figure having the colored appearance of the complementary of the exposed stimulus.

There are many subtleties to the measurements of these color phenomena. For example, the exact color that is imposed on the grey center patch in simultaneous color contrast will depend on the intensity of the colored stimulus and the intensity of the grey area. Therefore, the simultaneous contrast color may not be identical to the complementary color. A second fact of considerable theoretical interest in color vision is that the apparent hue of a particular wavelength is dependent on the intensity of the monochromatic light. There are only three regions of the spectrum that do not change color with increasing intensity, 572 mμ (yellow), 503 mμ (green), and 478 mμ (blue). All the remaining regions undergo some color change. This phenomenon is called the Bezold-Brücke effect. Phenomena of this sort provide a rich source of intricate details that must be taken into account in analyzing the complex stimuli available in everyday use of the visual system.

SOME TOPICS IN PERCEPTION

Contrast Effects

We have just had occasion to refer to simultaneous color contrast. This is just one of a set of contrast phenomena. Perhaps a more common form is simultaneous brightness contrast.

Suppose we present two equally illuminated semicircular areas to a subject's two eyes in such a way that the left eye sees one half-circle, the right eye sees the other half-circle, and the two are so placed that the subject sees a full circle with two equally bright halves. If we now surround the semicircle in the right eye with a bright area, the two halves of the circle will no longer appear equal. The semicircle with the bright surround will appear dimmer. This reduction in brightness, resulting from a neighboring brighter region, is called simultaneous contrast. The magnitude of this contrast effect, that is, the amount of reduction in the apparent intensity of the semicircle, will depend on the intensity of the surrounding field. The intensity of the surrounding field has little effect on the appearance of the center field until the surrounding intensity is made greater than the center intensity. For all higher intensities the brightness of the center goes down in proportion to the increase in the surrounding intensity. The magnitude of the decrease in brightness in simultaneous contrast also depends on the size of the neighboring stimulus and on the distance between the two fields.

These contrast effects lead us to see many things that, in a sense, are not there. Not only are there systematic changes in what brightness pairs are called equal, but we shall see gradients of brightness in regions that have uniform light output.

It is clear that living organisms must move and act in a three-dimensional world, and we have several sensory systems for detecting the spatial arrangements of objects in space. In discussing visual acuity we have already referred to our ability to detect differences in position in the plane perpendicular to our line of sight, that is, to the left and right or up and down. Such visual cues can be utilized with either one eye or two, but they require only one eye. They are therefore called *monocular cues*. Most of the techniques used by artists to portray depth in a two-dimensional drawing are based on the monocular cues we use in responding to the three-dimensional world in which we live. The major monocular cues are size, contrast, parallax, and interposition.

An object of fixed size will subtend a smaller and smaller visual angle as its distance increases. This visual angle may be used in a variety of ways as a cue to depth. For objects of known size the relative size in a stimulus complex provides important information about distance. If a man appears larger than a house we will usually report that the man is closer than the house; if he is about the same size as the door of the house we will report them as being at the same distance; if he is small compared to the size of the door or window we will say that the man is farther away than the house. A special case of this relative size cue is linear perspective; this is a condition in which parallel contours are seen as converging as they recede from us. Railroad tracks, sides of roads, telephone wires, sides of houses and many other parallel contours found in our culture provide good examples of this principle. This cue of relative size also operates in more irregular patterns, for example, in the gradients of texture or graininess seen in large surfaces of rocks or pebbles. Some examples of these cues are illustrated in Figure 1-17.

The contrast of an object and its background also provides us with information about distance. The more distant an object is, the more the atmosphere attenuates or reduces the visibility of the contrasting brightness of the stimulus and its surrounding field. We see an extreme example of this in the case of fog, but it operates at all times. The large errors we make in estimating distance when we change climatic conditions are impressive; an individual skilled in estimating distances in the eastern parts of the United States will make large and systematic errors in his estimates of distance in some regions in the West where the atmospheric attenuation is much less.

Cues derived from movement parallax arise in two ways, (1) when the observer moves with respect to the objects being viewed and (2) when the objects being viewed move with respect to the observer. Two stationary objects at different distances from the eye will move with respect to each other if the eye moves. For example, a farm house and a tree at different distances from the observer will change their relative positions when viewed from a moving train. On a smaller scale it is frequently possible to tell whether two objects are at different distances simply by moving the head to the left and right. An alternative form of this parallax principle is that two objects moving at the same speed, but at different distances, will change their relative positions when the eye is stationary.

Interposition is probably the simplest and most obvious of the monocular

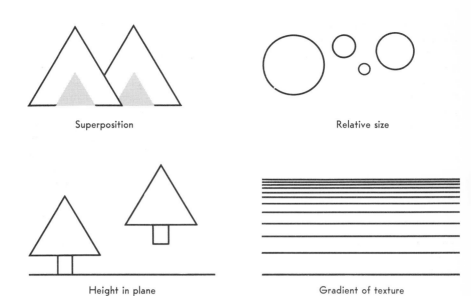

Superposition

Relative size

Height in plane

Gradient of texture

Figure 1-17.   Illustrations of monocular cues to distance. Examples of these cues appear in the photograph below. (Photo courtesy of Ansel Adams.)

cues. Simply stated, a near object will obscure a far object if the two are along the same line of sight and the near one is opaque.

A second class of cues that we use for detecting and estimating distances arises from the interaction of the two eyes. At very short distances the information coming from the muscles that converge the two eyes may help us in making distance discriminations, but this cue is probably not very important for distances beyond arm's length. The most important binocular information comes in the form of stereoscopic vision. Stereoscopic vision is based on the fact that the two eyes are located at different positions in space, yet their fields of view overlap. We possess this compelling cue to depth because our two eyes are able to image the same regions of the environment and because the eye muscles normally coordinate the eyes so that they fixate on the same point in the environment. Each eye receives a slightly different view of the environment. Normally these differences are small and are seen, not as two different views, but as a single scene with depth. With certain disorders of the eye muscles, in which the eyes do not normally fixate at the same point, the difference in the views is too large. Under these circumstances a person cannot fuse the separate impressions to the two eyes; in this case the visual apparatus usually suppresses one view and essentially operates as a one-eye system.

The geometry of stereoscopic vision is similar to that encountered in parallax phenomena. This can be illustrated by an inspection of Figure 1-18. Light from two objects, A and B, strikes the left and right eye at A_L and A_R and B_L and B_R respectively. Because these objects are at different distances, angles a and b are different; elementary trigonometry then tells us that angles c and d are different. These angular differences provide us with the kind of spatial information that we use in studies of visual acuity. However, it is a special kind of acuity because it involves the two eyes.

It is easier to illustrate the problem by discussing a special case. Imagine looking down a tunnel that has a stationary rod hanging from the ceiling and extending down to the level of the eye. Imagine a second rod sticking up from the floor so that it almost meets the upper rod. This bottom rod is mounted on a track so that it can be moved closer and further away. Let us now line up our left eye so that it is at one end of the track; in this case the lower rod will not move left and right with respect to the upper rod as we change its distance. However, the view we receive in the right eye changes systematically with the relative distance of the two rods. As the lower rod moves nearer, its image in the right eye moves laterally to the

Figure 1-18. Geometrical representation of the disparity of the retinal images in the two eyes when we view two objects at different distances from the eyes.

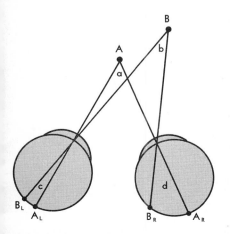

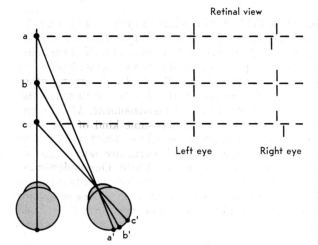

Retinal view

Left eye   Right eye

Figure 1-19. Geometrical arrangement involved in binocular cues to depth when the changes in distance are always along the line of sight of one eye.

right relative to the image of the upper rod; as the lower rod moves farther away its image moves to the left relative to the image of the upper rod. Figure 1-19 shows the image arrangement for three views, (1) with the lower rod "nearer," (2) with the lower rod "farther," and (3) with the upper and lower rods at the same distance. Our ability to tell whether two objects are at the same distance is therefore dependent on our ability to judge the equality of two angles. The judgment is more complicated than monocular acuity because it requires a comparison between the two eyes. This kind of acuity is called stereoscopic acuity.

Illusions

Let us turn finally to a set of visual stimuli that are grouped together because they are said to produce illusions. An illusion is usually thought of as a "false" perception. This notion of a "false" perception is a deceptively simple conception; it seems satisfactory on first reading, but its meaning is uncertain as we begin to look at the problem more carefully. The kind of stimulus figures that are usually considered to produce illusions are illustrated in Figure 1-20. These figures, in general, establish that under certain circumstances one sees a straight line as curved, or sees the longer of two lines as being shorter, and so on. Such observations are consistent with the usual definition of illusion; we are not seeing the world as it really is. We run into difficulty when we attempt to set these figures off from the kinds of stimuli discussed earlier. It is quite clear that we rarely observe a direct linear correspondence between the environment as it is described by the physical sciences and the action of our sensory systems, whether studied behaviorally or physiologically. We have seen many examples of situations in which the visual system fails to render the characteristics that we know exist in the environment. For example, we have seen that a light source which is alternately on and off may be seen as flickering under some conditions and may be seen as steady under others. Two separate lights may be judged equal in brightness when they are the only lights in the environment but may be judged as unequal if one of the lights has a bright surrounding field. A dim white stimulus patch may be grey when no other stimuli are present but may assume a greenish appearance if it is surrounded by a red light or may appear as reddish if surrounded by a green light. A light that will appear to be dim to the light-adapted eye will appear quite bright to a dark-adapted eye. We could give many other examples of these complex relations between what subjects say they see and the actual physical characteristic of the stimulating environment. Most of the illusion figures are simply classical examples of this same kind of phenomenon. In the Mueller-Lyer illusion, for example, two lines which under most circumstances would be judged as being of equal length are not judged as equally long if additional lines are placed in the visual field. Our understanding of the mechanisms involved in the perception of such figures is far from complete. However, it is important to understand that these figures do not pose a new kind of question; they simply pose a more complicated question.

Figure 1-20. Geometrical illusions. (A) Circles 1 and 2 are really the same size. (B) Segments 1, 2, 3, and 4 are all the same length. (C) The two crescents are the same size. (D) The two horizontal lines are parallel the whole distance.

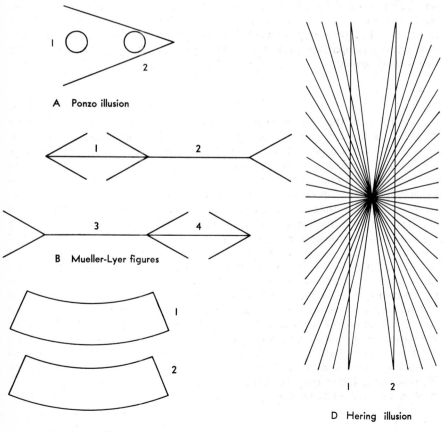

A Ponzo illusion

B Mueller-Lyer figures

C Jastrow illusion

D Hering illusion

Physiological Mechanisms
in Vision

If we look at the variety of living forms around us, we find many structures that qualify as eyes. These differ greatly in complexity, and among the most complex is the human eye. Since the neural layers of the human eye are, embryologically, an outgrowth of the brain, they exhibit many of the complexities of brain structure and brain activity. In gross outline, however, the structures of the eye may be rather simply represented. A schematic depiction of the human eye is shown in Figure 2-1. The light enters the eye at the cornea, passes through a viscous material called the aqueous humor, then through the pupil, an opening

30

2

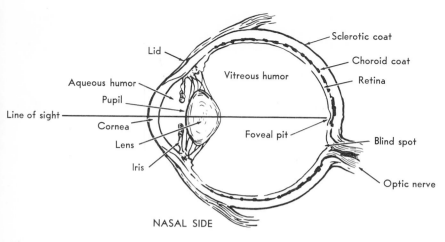

Figure 2-1. Schematic representation of the structures of the eye.

formed by the muscular structures called the iris. The light proceeds through the lens and another viscous material, called the vitreous humor, and finally passes into several layers of tissue collectively called the retina. These retinal layers contain the sense cells for vision and an elaborate network of nerve tissue, including the ganglion cells whose axons make up the fibers of the optic nerve and optic tract. A representation of some of the connections in these retinal layers is shown in Figure 2-2.

Figure 2-2. Structural arrangement of the cells in the retina. (S.R. Detwiler. Sigma Xi Quarterly, *1941, 29, 112–129.)*

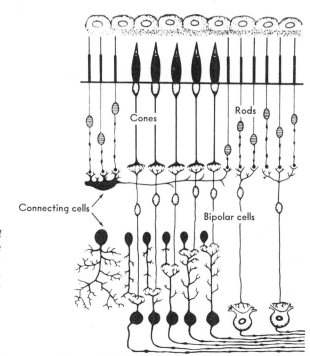

When we first encounter a detailed description of the layers of the retina, our impression is that the retina is arranged backwards. The sensitive elements that absorb the light are as far away from the source of light as they can get and still be in the retina. In other words, light has to pass through all the nerve layers of the retina before it can reach the outer parts of the sense cell where it is absorbed. Fortunately, these intervening structures are remarkably transparent, so that appreciable amounts of light entering the eye do, in fact, reach the sense cells. Even so, it is estimated that about half of the light hitting the cornea is lost before it reaches the sense cells.

We have already had occasion to comment that the data on visibility, illustrated in Figures 1-1 and 1-3, lead to the conclusion that we have two visual systems. This has been confirmed histologically. There are two major types of sense cells in the retina of man, the rods and the cones. The rods are not found in the very center of the retina, the fovea, but are found in large numbers in the periphery. The rods seem to provide the mechanism for scotopic vision, yielding the curves labeled S in Figures 1-1 and 1-3. The cones provide the physiological mechanism for the photopic function, the curves labeled P in Figures 1-1 and 1-3. Over intermediate ranges of intensity for regions of the retina outside the fovea we undoubtedly are served by some mixture of these two systems.

PHOTOCHEMISTRY: THE RHODOPSIN CYCLE

One question we might ask is about how the light is absorbed and utilized by the sense cells. During the nineteenth century it was demonstrated that a chemical substance exists in the sensitive layers of the retina that is bleached by light. The material was later isolated and many of its photochemical and biochemical properties became known. This substance is called rhodopsin and it is found in the external segments of the rods. Bombarding this material with light begins a sequence of chemical changes, leading first to the breakdown of rhodopsin and eventually to its regeneration. This visual cycle of decomposition and regeneration of rhodopsin is shown in Figure 2-3. The first major step in this sequence of reactions is the changing of rhodopsin to retinene, via two intermediate stages called lumi-rhodopsin and meta-rhodopsin. The second major step in the cycle is the conversion of retinene to Vitamin A. The latter reaction is under the control of a well-known enzyme system. Under normal physiological conditions these two major steps are reversible, that is, retinene is reformed from Vitamin A and rhodopsin is reformed from retinene.

The importance of rhodopsin for seeing is now clearly established. The amount of light absorbed by rhodopsin at different wavelengths agrees almost exactly with the scotopic visibility curve. It is generally agreed that the visibility of different wavelengths in the periphery of the dark-adapted eye is an expression of the absorption characteristics of rhodopsin.

Since rhodopsin is bleached by light and will regenerate in the dark, it seems natural to suppose that we have an easy explanation for the data of light- and dark-adaptation. There is much to recommend this interpretation.

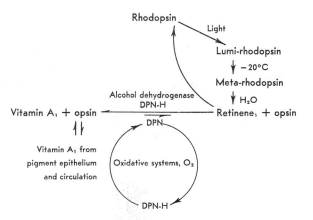

Figure 2-3. Schematic representation of one of the photochemical systems in the eye. (R. Hubbard and G. Wald. Proc. nat. Acad. Sci., 37, 69. Washington, D.C.: 1951.)

The times required for bleaching and regeneration are of the right order of magnitude; it takes as long as an hour to get complete regeneration of rhodopsin after bleaching with a bright light. In addition, the rate of breakdown is more rapid than the rate of regeneration of rhodopsin from Vitamin A. This observation agrees with the relative speeds of light- and dark-adaptation studied psychophysically. Because of these parallels it is tempting to think of the decreased sensitivity we observe in the light-adapted eye as being due to the depletion of the material that absorbs the light. Conversely, the increased sensitivity in the dark-adapted eye could then be thought of as being due to the abundance of absorbing material. With very little material available to absorb the incoming light energy, we would need a large amount of light in order to produce a given amount of change in the absorbing material; with a large amount of rhodopsin available we would need much less light to produce the same amount of change in the absorbing material.

Although the gross qualitative predictions from this notion are correct, the interpretation encounters some quantitative difficulties. Recent measurements in the intact human eye have shown that the changes in concentration during dark-adaptation do not exceed about 20 or 30 per cent, while the threshold in the same experiment changes by a factor of a thousand or more. These results do not mean that the first step in the process of seeing is not photochemical; we know that it is. These measurements do mean that we do not yet have an adequate interpretation of the linkage between these photochemical changes and the changes in threshold. As we shall see later, this lack of agreement is not surprising, because these chemical changes must activate the nervous system and there are many properties of the nervous system that undoubtedly leave their mark on the working of the total system.

Much less is known about the photochemical materials that take part in vision involving the cones. A material called iodopsin has been extracted from vertebrate eyes. It seems to participate in a visual cycle analogous to that for rhodopsin. It has an absorption curve that agrees approximately with the photopic visibility curve and it may provide the physiological mechanism for photopic visibility.

It is obvious that we must go beyond a consideration of the photochemistry of visual substances to find an appropriate mechanism for many of the psychophysical functions we have discussed. Whenever we change the size of the stimulus, or study problems of acuity, or the contrast effects so typical of human vision, we are undoubtedly bringing into play complex interactions among individual sensory elements and nerve cells in the retina. The complexities of the nervous interconnections in the retina and in higher brain centers should immediately alert us to the possibility that it will not be easy to unravel the nature of this nervous interaction. This is particularly true if we try to start this investigation in the human retina.

The sense cells in the retina are very small, one to two microns in diameter and perhaps 10 microns in length. They are tightly packed together and there are about 125,000,000 of them in the human retina. About 120 million of these are rods, about 5 million are cones. These sense cells are the first stage in the visual system. The second stage in the passage of information in the visual system is a layer in the retina containing cells that are called bipolar cells. These are also very small nerve cells, perhaps ten microns in length. These bipolar cells then connect with ganglion cells whose extensions make up the nerve fibers in the optic nerve. Thus, the nerve fibers in man's optic nerve are third-order neurons; they are the third link in the chain from the sense cell to the brain. The links are, in order, sense cells, bipolar cells, ganglion cells. The system in the vertebrate retina is additionally complicated by two other types of cells, the amacrine and horizontal cells. These cells are not part of the most direct progression from sense cells to ganglion cells. They are like trunk lines; they run primarily laterally and offer many possibilities for the interaction of the information that comes from adjacent sets of sense cells.

It is a big step to go from the study of the properties of a chemical substance that can be extracted from many thousands of cells and obtained in rather large quantities to a study of the functioning of a single sense cell whose extensions may only measure several microns in length. The experimental meaning of a micron in length may be appreciated if we stop to realize that this is about the theoretical limit of the best light microscope; this is true because we are looking at things whose dimensions are about equal to the wavelength of the light we are using to see them ($.7 \mu$ is the same as 700 mμ, which is the wavelength of red light.) But since ingenuity in science seems to know no bounds, we shall be discussing results obtained with small electrodes whose diameter at the tip can only be measured with an electron microscope. However, these are relatively recent developments and there are still technical difficulties in placing the electrodes where we want them in the retina. As a result our most complete knowledge of the kinds of nerve messages conducted in first-order nerve fibers comes from work on lower animals.

One of the most important steps in analyzing neural mechanisms in vision was taken when Graham and Hartline first reported on the kind of nerve messages found in single fibers in the optic nerves of compound eyes. These eyes are found in many lower forms, such as the insects. Compound eyes differ markedly from the human eye and some of these differences provide distinct advantages in our study of the visual system. For example, these eyes are made up of many individual facets, called ommatidia, that are closely packed together. Each of these ommatidia has its own lens system. Out of these ommatidia, nerve fibers run without interruption to the optic lobe. Thus, nerve fibers traveling in the optic nerve of these animals make direct contact with the sense cell. If one records from a fiber in the optic nerve of these animals one is looking at information traveling in a neuron that connects directly with the sensory apparatus. The fact that each ommatidium has its own lens system makes it easy to stimulate a single sensory unit. Thus, one can obtain a picture of nerve activity that is free of some of the complexity that is so abundant in the retina of man.

Before discussing the kind of messages carried in optic nerve fibers, we might digress at this point to summarize a few characteristics of nerve conduction. Under normal physiological conditions information is transmitted along individual nerve fibers in the form of nerve impulses. The phrase nerve impulse is a summary term for a brief series of electrical and chemical changes that travel along a nerve process at a speed dependent on the size of the fiber and the nature of the covering material, or sheathing, of the fiber. A normal nerve fiber in a resting state maintains what is called a membrane potential, that is, the inside of this nerve is electrically negative with respect to the outside. When a nerve impulse passes, there is a rapid reversal of this membrane potential and a comparably rapid recovery to the original state. This reversible change proceeds down the nerve from the point of initiation to the end of the nerve fiber. An impulse, under normal physiological conditions, obeys what is called the all-or-none principle: If the impulse occurs at all, it occurs with its characteristic amplitude. This amplitude is large (perhaps 100 millivolts) for a large fiber, small for a fiber of small diameter. However, it does not vary with the intensity of the stimulus. Similarly the speed of travel of the nerve impulse is great for large fibers (about 100 meters a second) and slower for small fibers. Again, the speed does not depend on the intensity of the stimulus. The usual technique for measuring the occurrence of an impulse is to measure changes in voltage associated with the impulse. These changes in potential can be amplified and recorded on film or photographic paper.

We have said that neither the magnitude of the nerve impulse nor its speed of conduction depends on the intensity of the stimulus; therefore, the fiber must have other ways of coding the nature of the stimulus presented. It achieves this by variations in the number of impulses and the frequency with which they occur.

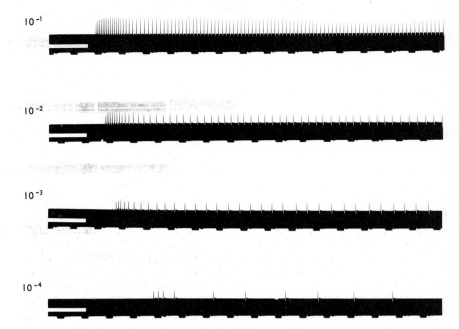

10^{-1}

10^{-2}

10^{-3}

10^{-4}

Figure 2-4. Response of a single optic nerve fiber in a compound eye to four different light intensities. (Courtesy of H.K. Hartline.)

Records of nerve activity, such as those in Figure 2-4, show the impulse as a black vertical line above the base line. Time is proceeding from left to right in the figure and the marks in the baseline indicate the time in fifths of seconds. The impulses appear as a thin line because of the nature of the time scale; if we were to increase the recording speed so that we could clearly mark off milliseconds on the time line, the electrical changes that take place as the impulse passes the recording electrodes would spread out on our record and would take on the appearance of the trace in Figure 2-5. If we were interested in studying the nature of the nerve impulse itself, we would have to magnify our time scale. Since, under normal physiological conditions, we know that all of these traces would look alike, we can for our purposes collapse the time scale and ignore the exact shape, or waveform, of these electrical changes.

Let us return now to the kinds of nerve messages we obtain from single first-order nerve cells in the visual system of the compound eye. We find that when we turn a light on and leave it on the response begins, after a short delay, and continues as long as the light is on. The upper line in Figure 2-4 is a record

Figure 2-5. A sequence of four nerve impulses in a single nerve fiber, showing the wave form of each impulse.

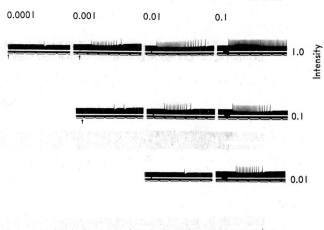

Figure 2-6. The impulse response of a single optic nerve fiber from a compound eye to stimuli of different durations and different intensities. Intensity is expressed in arbitrary units, duration in seconds. (H.K. Hartline. J. cell. comp. Physiol., 1934, 5, 229–247.)

obtained using a very high intensity, the lowest line is one obtained using a dim intensity, the intermediate lines represent two intermediate intensities. The short delay between the onset of the light and the first impulse in the response is called the latency. The records in this figure illustrate the following general facts: (1) The higher the intensity of the stimulus the shorter the latency, (2) for any intensity the impulses will occur more frequently when the light has just been turned on than after it has been on for a few seconds or a few minutes, (3) the higher the intensity the greater the rate at which the impulses are generated once they start, and (4) the higher the intensity the more rapidly the fiber will respond once it reaches its terminal steady frequency.

If the light is on for a short time the nerve will respond for a brief period and stop. The total number of impulses in the burst of responding will depend on the intensity and the duration of the stimulus. For exposures shorter than one second, the manner in which the response is affected by intensity and duration of the stimulus is shown in Figure 2-6. If we read up from the bottom in any of the columns of Figure 2-6, we see the effect of increasing intensity while the exposure time is kept fixed. If we read across any row of records, we see the effect of increasing the exposure time when the intensity is fixed. It is interesting to note the similarity between the results in this figure and the psychophysical results discussed previously when we described the Bunsen-Roscoe law. As you will recall, we found that a constant product of intensity and duration was required in order to reach threshold. The records along any left-to-right diagonal in Figure 2-6 represent fixed amounts of energy (fixed products of intensity and exposure time); it is obvious that the response is fixed regardless of individual values of intensity or duration of the stimulus, as long as the product of these two is a constant. Thus, the Bunsen-Roscoe law holds for durations less than 0.1 second, which corresponds closely to human psychophysical data.

It is also possible to show the processes of dark- and light-adaptation in single optic nerve fibers. If the eye is first light-adapted, then placed in the dark, and a brief test stimulus is presented at various times after the adapting light is turned off, there is a gradual increase in the amount of responding to a fixed intensity stimulus. A series of records obtained during dark-adaptation is shown in Figure 2-7. Clearly, the sense cell is getting more and more sensitive with time in the dark. If we measure the intensity required to give a constant response at various stages of dark-adaptation we obtain curves quantitatively similar to those shown in Figure 1-5.

We can also measure the visibility curve for these single sensory units. Recall that we obtain visibility curves for a human subject by measuring the intensity required at different wavelengths to produce a fixed response, usually a fixed probability of detecting the stimulus. We can also measure the energy required at different wavelengths to obtain a fixed response for a single sensory unit in the compound eye. The nerve responses obtained at seven different wavelengths are shown in Figure 2-8A. In this case a fixed response of seven impulses was selected; similar results can be obtained using other fixed magnitudes of response. The first column of numbers in this figure represents the wavelengths used, the second column gives the relative intensities required. As in the experiments with the human observer we find that more intensity is required at the extremes of the visible spectrum to elicit a response than is required in the middle of the spectrum. If we take the reciprocals of the intensity values shown in the second column of Figure 2-8A and plot these values as we did in the case of the data from human subjects, we obtain the visibility curve shown by the solid line in Figure 2-8B. This figure is similar to the data from human discrimination shown by curve S in Figure 1-3. We could review many more examples of this parallelism between the results of the human psychophysical experiments and the action in single sensory units.

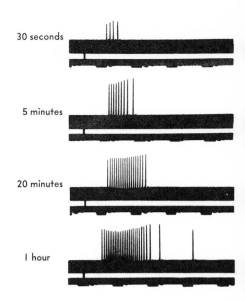

Figure 2-7. The response of a single optic nerve fiber at different stages during dark-adaptation. A test flash of a fixed intensity and of .01 second duration was presented at the indicated times after cessation of the adapting stimulus. The test stimuli are indicated by breaks in the white bars. (H.K. Hartline. J. opt. Soc. Amer., 1940, 30, 239–247.)

Nerve Activity in the Vertebrate Visual System

We have said that the advantages of working with nerve fibers from the compound eye are that it is possible to stimulate single sensory units and that the first-order neurons are relatively long. In the vertebrate retina, as we have already noted, the first-order neurons are only a few microns in length. These then connect with the bipolar cells which are also very small. Not until we reach the ganglion cells, which mark the third link in the chain, do we encounter cells that have yielded to the experimental attack of impulse recording.

The responses we measure in these third-order axons exhibit a complexity that we do not usually find in first-order neurons, but it is a kind of complexity with which we must be prepared to deal. This complexity shows itself in one very important way. The type of nerve response we have discussed so far is what is called an "on" response. The nerve is "quiet" as long as no light is present. When the light is turned on the fiber begins to transmit impulses and continues to transmit impulses as long as the light is on. When the light is turned off, the impulses cease. When we look at the types of responses we get from single nerve fibers in the vertebrate retina, such as the fibers in the optic nerve of the frog, or

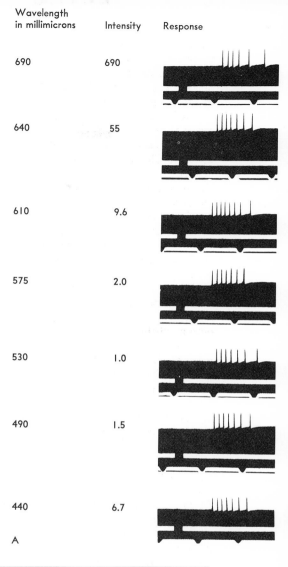

Wavelength in millimicrons	Intensity	Response
690	690	
640	55	
610	9.6	
575	2.0	
530	1.0	
490	1.5	
440	6.7	

A

Figure 2-8. Visibility data from a single optic nerve fiber. (A) This figure shows the extent to which the nerve response is the same for all stimulus wavelengths if the experimenter adjusts the intensity appropriately (see text). (B) The visibility curve as a function of wavelength based on the data from (A). (C.H. Graham and H.K. Hartline. J. gen. Physiol., 1935, 18, 917–931.)

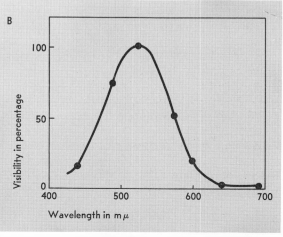

cat, or monkey, we find that there are three kinds of response. One is an "on" type of response similar to the one we just described; another is an "on-off" response, the third is an "off" response. In the "on-off" response when the light is turned on there is a brief burst of impulses, but this firing stops even if the light stays on. When the light is turned off, however, there is another burst of activity that quickly subsides and then no further activity is seen until the light is turned on again. In the "off" type of response the fiber does not respond when the light is turned on; nor does it respond while the light is on; but when the light is turned off there is a burst of impulses that quickly stops after a short period of darkness. This "off" response can be inhibited by turning on the light again.

Originally it was thought that these categories of "on," "on-off," and "off" represented three separate types of fibers. In the species first studied, the type of response shown by each individual neuron was extremely stable; under a large range of conditions the neuron showed one characteristic type of response and no other. More recent work on the higher vertebrates, however, has shown that individual nerve fibers are labile and can give either an "on" response or an "off" response depending on test conditions. These "on" and "off" responses seem to be part of an elaborate antagonistic system that pits excitatory and inhibitory systems against one another.

One thing that may seem puzzling is that the responses at all stages of the visual system from the optic nerve to the brain seem to emphasize changes in stimulation. Most of the responding occurs when the stimulus changes either its intensity or its position; we get little activity to steady stimulation; three-quarters of the fibers respond chiefly to transient stimulation. Yet we know that in human vision we rarely completely adapt to a visual stimulus. If you fixate on a letter or word on this page and look at it continuously it never disappears as long as you keep your eyes open and stay awake. At first glance these facts seem inconsistent. However, the measurements taken of our ability to fixate seem to resolve this conflict. If we ask a subject to look at a point in the environment and then measure the position of the eye very carefully, we find that although the subject is very good at being *approximately* on target, the eye is always in motion. Small oscillations are always present as the eye is aimed at the fixation point. These represent a type of ocular tremor. The oscillations are small, being less than one minute of visual angle. They are also very rapid, occurring at a rate of about 50 to 100 times a second. Because of these rapid movements the image of an object is constantly being swept across the sense cells. Individual sense cells, therefore, are being exposed to rapidly changing intensities when a person looks at a steady environment, provided there are intensity differences in the environment.

The importance of these small eye movements for human vision can be shown dramatically by using a special optical system that stabilizes the image on the retina. This may be done using a technique such as is shown in Figure 2-9. A subject is asked to view a stimulus figure that is projected onto a screen. The unusual feature of the apparatus is that the optics of the projection system include a small mirror that is attached to the cornea of the eye. One of the simplest ways of doing so is to fit the subject with contact lenses and mount the mirror on the contact lens. If we adjust the length of the optical path appropriately, as shown in Figure 2-9, it is possible to present a

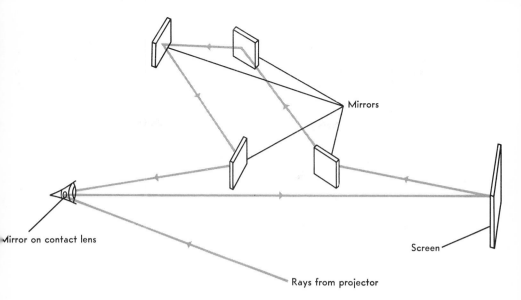

Figure 2-9. Schematic representation of one procedure for presenting a motionless image on the human retina. (L.A. Riggs, F. Ratliff, J.C. Cornsweet, and T. Cornsweet. J. opt. Soc. Amer., 1953, 43, 495.)

stabilized image on the retina. Whenever the eye moves the projected stimulus configuration moves in a direction, and by an amount, such that the image is stationary on the retina. The surprising result of such a procedure is this: The subject will report that a stimulus, clearly visible when first presented, will lose all its contours after about one minute of observation. These results suggest that we see the steady aspects of the visual environment by the rather unlikely combination of two physiological systems; we have a sensory system that is primarily responsive to rapid changes in light intensity and we have an auxiliary system that transforms steady gradients of intensity into rapidly changing ones on the retina.

Because of the elaborate interconnections among the cells of the retina, the cells in the optic nerve in vertebrate eyes are not limited to responding only when a single sensory unit is stimulated. Each nerve fiber can be activated by focusing the light anywhere over a wide area. This area is called the receptive field of the nerve fiber. The size of this field depends on the intensity of the exploring light. If we map the receptive field with a weak stimulus, the region in which we can elicit a response is small; if we map the receptive field with a strong light, the effective region is large. These receptive fields are elliptical in shape and the maps obtained using different intensities are all arranged concentrically. The center of the receptive field of the particular fiber is always the most sensitive region.

Audition   The kinds of stimuli that
we associate with hearing include such sounds as speech,
musical notes, and noise. These sounds produce relatively
rapid changes in pressure in the air, and many of the
pressure changes we hear, when analyzed in detail, have
an oscillatory character. For example, the pressure changes
that result when we make a vowel sound, such as *ah* or *ee*,
or when we play middle C on a clarinet or violin, are
cyclical. The pitch of such sounds comes from the
oscillatory, or repetitive, nature of the pressure changes.
In addition to being able to tell that middle C on the
clarinet and the violin have the same pitch, however,

3

we are able to tell that these two notes come from different musical instruments. We seem to be able to achieve this discrimination on the basis of the particular waveform that is being repeated. If we are to understand the meaning and importance of these properties of hearing, we must look more closely at some of the techniques for describing auditory stimuli.

Probably all of us have an intuitive notion of what the words "frequency" and "harmonics" mean. Unfortunately for most of us, this intuitive notion is not powerful enough to carry us through many of the specific problems we meet in the study of audition, so we shall have to strengthen it. When we think of something as periodic, or repetitive, we think of it as repeating itself over and over again, whether it is the simple swing of a pendulum or the more complex repetitions found in musical sounds. The basic problem we face in our search for a precise definition of a term such as frequency is two-fold; how long is "over and over again" and what is the waveform that is repeated? Intuitively, we would all probably agree that if the simple oscillation shown in Figure 3-1A went on forever we would call it periodic. We might not know exactly what to say if we were asked if the curves in Figure 3-1B and 3-1C

Figure 3-1. Three possible auditory stimuli. The left part shows the magnitude of the pressure as a function of time for the three signals. The right part shows the associated spectrum for these three signals.

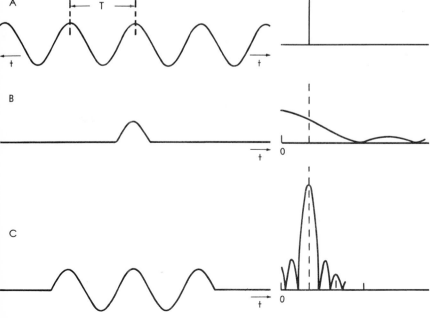

Time

Frequency in cycles per second

were periodic. This is the problem, for these are actually segments of the waveform in 3-1A.

The Sinusoid

Let us digress for a moment and define a few terms. We have said that we hear relatively rapid changes in pressure. The most obvious way of describing these is to plot the pressure as a function of time, that is, to show how the instantaneous pressure changes from moment to moment. This plot will help us decide whether the pressure is changing rapidly and how it is changing. When we do this we say we have plotted an amplitude-time function because, indeed, we have plotted how the amplitude of the pressure varies as a function of time. Now, sound sources produce changes in pressure in the air by moving. Therefore, there is an alternate way of describing the changes produced by a sound source; instead of measuring the pressure, we can describe displacement of the molecules in the air. Since there is an exact mathematical relation between pressure and displacement, it is always possible to convert one of these measures into the other. In this chapter we shall usually use the dimension of pressure. We mention the term displacement at this point because it is useful in explaining another very common term in hearing, the *sinusoid*. Many physical systems such as a swing or pendulum or a taut string will, if moved from their resting position and released, move back to their resting position in a characteristic way. We are all familiar with the swing which, when released from a displaced position, will move toward its resting position. It will move slowly at first, then rapidly, reaching its maximum speed when it passes through its resting position. It will overshoot the resting position. As it does so it will begin to slow down, then finally stop, and begin to move in the opposite direction. This process is repeated until it finally comes to rest. If we plotted how far away from the resting position the swing is at every moment in time, we would find that it traces out a path that is very similar to a curve called a sinusoid. This displacement curve would be very similar to the curve we have shown in Figure 3-1A, which is one of the trigonometric curves—for example, a sine or cosine curve. The phrase "very similar" is used because the curve we obtain from the swing is not quite a pure sinusoid; the swing will gradually "die down" and stop. Any system with friction will do so. Such a curve is called a "damped" sinusoid because the amplitudes of successive swings are gradually decreasing.

A purer example of a sinusoid is illustrated by Figure 3-2. Imagine a wheel attached to the shaft of a constant-speed motor and a pen attached to the end of one spoke by a yoke arrangement as shown in Figure 3-2. As the wheel rotates, the pen moves vertically in a manner dictated by the changing magnitude of A in Figure 3-2. The value of A will depend on the angle, θ. When θ is zero, A will be zero. We usually express the changes in θ in one of two ways, either in degrees or in radians. A radian is an angle whose intersected arc on the circumference of a circle is equal in length to the radius of the circle. There are, therefore, 2π radians in a circle, which is easy to remember if you can remember that the circumference of a circle is $2\pi r$.

From elementary trigonometry we know that $\sin\theta$ is equal to A/R where R is the radius of the circle. This means that the height, A, is equal to $R\sin\theta$. Since the yoke rotates at a constant rate, angle θ will change at a

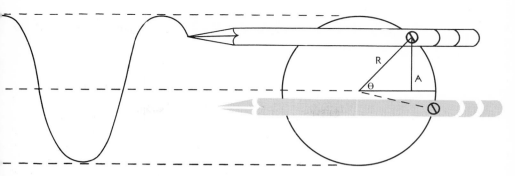

Figure 3-2. Schematic drawing of an apparatus for generating a sinusoidal wave (see text).

fixed rate too. The angle θ can therefore be expressed as a function of time.

If the wheel is rotating, say w turns per second, then θ will be changing at a rate of 360 w degrees per second, or $2\pi w$ radians per second. This means that we can substitute for θ in the equation for A in the following way:

$$A = R\sin\theta$$
$$A = R\sin 2\pi wt$$

Since R is the radius of the circle, it represents the height of the peak, and the greatest depth of the trough, of the sinusoid traced by the pen.

Fourier Analysis of Periodic Waveforms

Let us return to our original problem of how to describe events that are periodic, or repetitious. The basic techniques for doing this are found in the work of Fourier, a famous mathematician of the early nineteenth century. Stated briefly, Fourier showed that any mathematical function (with a few restrictions that are of no concern in analyzing physical systems) can be synthesized by summing a set of simple sinusoidal functions, that is, sine and cosine functions. How can we use this finding in the study of audition? First, let us avoid the difficulty of deciding how often a waveform should repeat itself to be called periodic by assuming that a function is periodic only (1) if it goes on forever and (2) if we can find a segment of it which, when repeatedly laid end to end, duplicates exactly the endless signal. This definition is illustrated in Figure 3-1A by the segment T; the endless sinusoid can be matched by taking an infinite number of segments, T, and laying them end to end. This commitment to endless signals seems like an unrealistic way to start to describe auditory signals, since we know that no actual auditory stimuli are endless. The strength of this step will become clear when we see what we can do with it. If we can find a segment, T, which, when repeated, will duplicate our endless signal, we call the length of time, T, the period. If the signal is a sinusoid, the reciprocal of the period, T, that is I/T, is called the *frequency* of the signal.

In applying these statements to the study of audition we would say that, when the pressure changes are sinusoidal and oscillate up and down slowly, then the period is large and the frequency is small; when the oscillation is

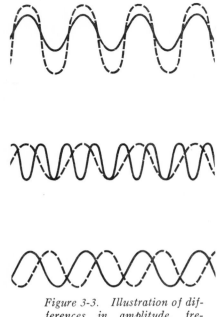

A

B

C

Figure 3-3. Illustration of differences in amplitude, frequency, and phase of a sinusoidal signal. (A) Two signals having the same frequency and phase but differing in amplitude. (B) Two signals having the same phase and amplitude but differing in frequency. (C) Two signals having the same amplitude and frequency but differing in phase.

rapid, the period is small and the frequency is large. If we have two sounds whose pressures go up and down equally rapidly but one has peaks and troughs that are higher and lower, we say that it has a greater *peak amplitude*. The only other item of information, other than the frequency and peak amplitude, that we need in order to specify the height of a sinusoidal curve at any and every moment in time is to know where it is in its oscillation at a particular moment in time. This gives us information about *phase*. Figure 3-3A shows two waves that have the same frequency and phase but have different amplitudes; Figure 3-3B shows two sinusoids that have the same amplitude but different frequencies; Figure 3-3C shows two sinusoids that have the same amplitude and frequency but different phases. The two curves in Figure 3-3C can be laid on top of one another by sliding one of them in time.

From our definition of periodic it should be quite clear that waveforms other than sinusoids may also be periodic, yet our definition of frequency assumes that the waves are sinusoidal. Therefore, we might ask what we are to say about the frequencies of non-sinusoidal waves. Here the work of Fourier is of paramount importance because he showed that complex waves can be reduced to a set of sinusoids, or can be formed by adding up a set of sinusoids. The only difference between an endless sinusoid and any other endless periodic function is that we need more than one sinusoid to synthesize the latter. We can appreciate how this Fourier analysis or synthesis works by looking at Figure 3-4A. The solid line, sometimes called a sawtooth waveform, is clearly not a sinusoid. A sine wave having the same repetition rate or period as the sawtooth is shown by the dotted line. Let us now direct our attention to just one period of vibration. If we select four sinusoids (one having the same period as the sawtooth, the others having periods equal to one-half, one-third, and one-fourth the period of the first sinusoid) and add all of these together, we get the wave form shown in Figure 3-4B. This gives us a closer approximation to the sawtooth. If we add to these sinusoids six more sinusoids whose periods are respectively, one-fifth, and so on, up to one-tenth the first, or fundamental, sinusoid, we obtain a better approximation to the sawtooth, as in Figure 3-4C. We can continue this addition until we achieve any degree

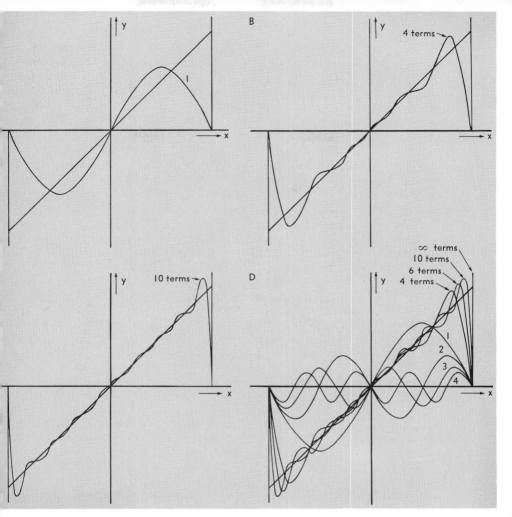

Figure 3-4 Successive approximations to a sawtooth wave as more sinusoidal components are added to the signal. (Modified from S. Goldman. Frequency analysis, modulation and noise. New York: McGraw-Hill, 1948.)

of approximation we please. If we take an infinite number of terms we get rid of all the rounded corners and then we actually duplicate the sawtooth wave. Some of the details of this addition process are shown in Figure 3-4D. Thus, if the sawtooth wave goes on forever we can duplicate it by taking a series of sinusoids that go on forever; the fundamental sinusoid has the same period as the sawtooth, and all of the other sinusoids have frequencies that are some multiple of the fundamental frequency.

Careful examination of Figure 3-4D will show that the harmonics, or the multiples of the fundamental, do not necessarily have the same amplitude as the fundamental. To duplicate all possible waveforms we must be free to pick the amplitude, frequency, and phase of the sinusoids to be added.

We need a short-hand expression for describing what we have just done. In our example, we have added together a series of sinusoids having different frequencies and different amplitudes. When we have determined the frequencies, and their respective amplitudes, required to duplicate a given waveform, we have arrived at what is called the frequency spectrum of the waveform. This is usually shown as a plot of the amplitude of all of the component frequencies needed to duplicate the waveform in which we are interested. The frequency spectrum of a repetitive sawtooth is called a line spectrum because this kind of signal can be handled by what is called the Fourier series. We do not always end up with a discrete spectrum. If we wish to duplicate a sound that has a finite duration, we must use the Fourier integral; in these cases we obtain what is called a continuous spectrum. Thus, the Fourier integral analysis permits us to free ourselves from the restriction of endless signals. When we determine the frequency spectrum of a waveform of finite duration, we find the set of endless sinusoids which, when added together, give us a sum that is (1) zero up to some particular time, (2) equivalent to our waveform for its duration, and then (3) zero for the rest of time. To achieve this result we need frequencies that are not all multiples of some fundamental frequency.

Let us summarize what we have said about frequency analysis. Any waveform that goes on forever and is periodic will have a frequency spectrum whose fundamental frequency is I/T and whose other frequency components are multiples of the fundamental frequency. How many, and which ones, of these harmonics we need will depend on the waveform we are analyzing. A plot of the magnitude of each frequency component yields the frequency spectrum of that particular signal. Any waveform that is of finite duration can also be considered to be the resultant of a set of endless sinusoids; in this case, however, the notion of a fundamental frequency is obscure because the waveform itself is not purely periodic. In this case the Fourier analysis yields a continuous spectrum, rather than a discrete one with measurable values only at multiples of some fundamental frequency.

One of the important properties of the Fourier analysis is that the linkage between the waveform and its frequency spectrum is a unique one; every waveform has its own frequency spectrum, and vice versa. Therefore, these are two completely equivalent descriptions of auditory stimuli. We are, therefore, free to turn to whichever description is most useful in any given experiment. For example, our observation that we can discriminate the differences between the middle C of a clarinet and the middle C of a violin can now be stated in two other ways. We can say that we can discriminate the waveforms or that we can discriminate the frequency spectra.

The Decibel

Let us conclude this section by introducing one other item of nomenclature. We have already seen that logarithmic dimensions are frequently used in sensory psychology. We find, for instance, that graphs of experimental data use the logarithm of intensity instead of the intensity, *per se*. In audition we find a special logarithmic scale, the decibel scale. The *decibel*, usually abbreviated db, is equivalent to one tenth of a bel. A *bel* is defined as the logarithm of the ratio of two measurements of power. The numerator of the ratio is the power of the particular stimulus one wishes to specify; the denominator is some arbitrary reference power level. Thus,

$$\text{bel} = \log \frac{P_{st}}{P_{ref}} \text{ and decibel} = 10 \log \frac{P_{st}}{P_{ref}}$$

The selection of the denominator is necessarily arbitrary. Several conventions have been adopted in practice. The most common practice now is to set the reference power equal to 10^{-16} watts.

Much of our discussion about the nature of audition will involve the dimension of pressure rather than power. Pressure measurements may also be converted to the decibel scale because the power of a sound is explicitly related to its pressure, being proportional to the square of the pressure. If we use pressure measurements in computing decibels, however, we must be careful to do one of two things; we must either square the pressure values before we take the logarithm or we must multiply the logarithm of the ratio by 20 instead of 10. This is a direct result of the nature of logarithms: The logarithm of a number that is squared is equivalent to twice the logarithm of the number. Thus,

$$\text{db} = 10 \log \frac{P_{st}}{P_{ref}} = 10 \log \frac{p^2_{st}}{p^2_{ref}} = 20 \log \frac{p_{st}}{p_{ref}}$$

THE MEASUREMENT OF AUDITORY THRESHOLDS

Audibility Curve

If we determine the absolute threshold for pure tones of various frequencies we obtain the results shown in Figure 3-5. This plot of absolute threshold as a function of the frequency of the auditory stimulus is called an audibility curve. Figure 3-5 shows that we are sensitive to pure tones in a range from approximately 15 or 20 cycles per second to about 15,000 or 20,000 cycles per second. To some extent both ends of this range are arbitrary. The lower end of this range raises the question of the subject's criterion for using "auditory" words in describing his sensations; the subject must decide at what point he should switch to using words such as "pulsating," "thumping," or "vibrating." The upper end of this scale depends importantly on the age of the subject tested. Frequencies around 100 cps seem to be unaffected by age differences at least up to the age of 60, while frequencies above 2000 cps begin to be affected by the age of the subject after he reaches 20. The normal person is most sensitive to frequencies in the region from 2000 to 4000 cps. He is less sensitive to frequencies above and below this range.

Duration of the Stimulus

Auditory thresholds of the sort plotted in Figure 3-5 are influenced by many variables. Several of these are analogous to variables discussed in the chapter on vision. The first of these

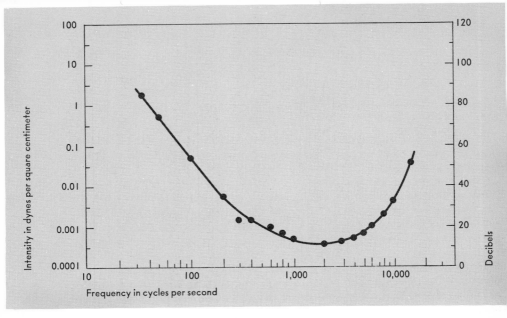

Figure 3-5. Audibility curve showing threshold intensity as a function of the frequency of the sinusoidal signal. (Modified from E.G. Wever. Theory of hearing. *New York: Wiley, 1949.)*

is the duration of the stimulus. As in vision, there is an inverse relation between the intensity required at threshold and the duration of the stimulus; the shorter the duration, the greater the intensity required for the subject to hear the stimulus.

An experiment on the duration of auditory stimuli is much more difficult to interpret than is its counterpart in vision. The reason for this difference involves our discussion of frequency analysis. You will recall that a tone is pure, in the sense of having only one frequency component, if the tone goes on forever. Although sinusoids of finite duration are not pure in this sense, we did find that a Fourier analysis could describe any short signal in terms of its frequency spectrum. One interesting consequence of such an analysis is that the shorter the duration of the stimulus, the more frequencies we need in order to describe it. Shortening the duration of a stimulus has the effect of spreading energy over many frequencies above and below what we might ordinarily consider to be the frequency. Such an analysis forces us to a surprising conclusion; it is not possible to study the effect of the duration of a stimulus having a single frequency component. As soon as the signal has finite duration it has more than one frequency component. This problem is not just an abstract theoretical issue that can be dismissed as irrelevant for human hearing. The problem shows itself in an important way in the psychophysical data in audition. We can illustrate this by examining the two curves in Figure 3-6. When we measure the relation between intensity and duration for a 4000-cps tone we obtain the curve labeled A. When we measure the same function for a 250-cps tone we obtain curve B. Obviously something

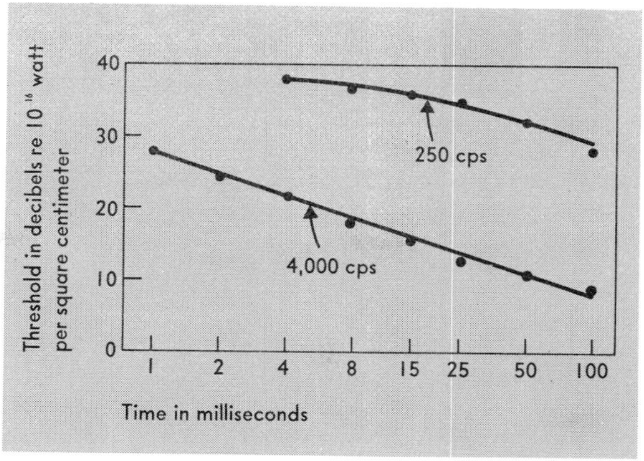

Figure 3-6. A graph of the change in the threshold intensity of a pure tone as a function of the duration of the tone. The results for a 250-cps and 4000-cps stimulus are shown. (W.R. Garner. J. acoust. Soc. Amer., 1947, 19, 808–815.)

different is happening to these two curves; the 250-cps curve begins to level off at short durations. It is as if duration no longer has an effect on the threshold for a tone when it is short. However, delivering a one millisecond exposure of a 250-cps tone is equivalent to delivering a stimulus whose wave form is like the curve in Figure 3-1C. The frequency spectrum of such a signal (also shown in Figure 3-1) tells us that there are appreciable amounts of energy for all frequencies from zero to several thousand cycles. Recall, however, that the audibility curve in Figure 3-5, which was obtained using long durations, has already demonstrated that we are relatively insensitive to 250 cps, but we are maximally sensitive to frequencies of several thousand cycles per second. Since the frequency analysis of a short 250-cps tone shows that there are appreciable amounts of energy at frequencies up to several thousand cycles per second, it is clear that the interpretation of the top curve in Figure 3-6 is complicated. Although the "true" intensity threshold may be increasing with decreasing duration, we may not be able to detect the increase because such a tone is delivering significant amounts of energy at frequencies for which our thresholds are lower. The net result is that the threshold becomes virtually independent of duration. This problem does not arise with the 10,000-cps curve because even a one millisecond exposure still presents ten complete cycles of the tone; such a waveform has a relatively sharply-peaked frequency spectrum as is shown in Figure 3-1B. This discussion serves as an important reminder that in sensory psychology there is an intricate interaction between the physical theory of the stimulus, the existing notions of the mechanism mediating the perception of stimuli, and the way we look at the behavioral data.

Auditory Fatigue and Masking

Another variable that influences the absolute threshold in audition is the amount of time since the last auditory stimulus. This effect is similar to the problem of dark-adaptation in vision and is usually referred to as auditory fatigue. If we are briefly exposed to the sound of an explosion or a jet engine, we know that our hearing is impaired while these stimuli are present. This impairment persists after the intense sound ceases. The recovery from brief exposures to intense sounds is rapid. This is illustrated in Figure 3-7; this shows the recovery from a brief half-second burst of noise at intensities of 80, 60, and 40 dbs. There is a very rapid drop within the first half-second, and an extrapolation of this curve would suggest that most of the recovery takes place in a few seconds.

From such observations we usually conclude that the adaptation effects in audition occur much more rapidly than in vision. Although it is difficult to make quantitative comparisons between sense modalities, two points may be noted: The first is that as we have already seen recovery from brief flashes of light is very rapid, the second is that long exposes to intense sounds also produce long-term changes in auditory thresholds. Although few auditory experiments have measured these long-term changes quantitatively. It is clear that the effects of intense auditory stimulation may persist for many hours.

We have just seen that intense sounds have after-effects that are similar to the adaptation effects of visual stimuli. Our ability to hear is also altered in the presence of such extraneous sounds. This is an example of what is called masking. More specifically, masking refers to the increase in threshold, or the decrease in sensitivity, due to the presence of another auditory stimulus at the time of the threshold measurement. Two main classes of stimuli have been used experimentally as masking stimuli, pure tones and noise. We can measure the masking effect that, say, a 1200-cps tone has on the thresholds for various frequencies in the audible spectrum by measuring (1) the threshold for each frequency when presented alone, and (2) the threshold for each of these frequencies in the presence of the 1200-cps masking tone. We use

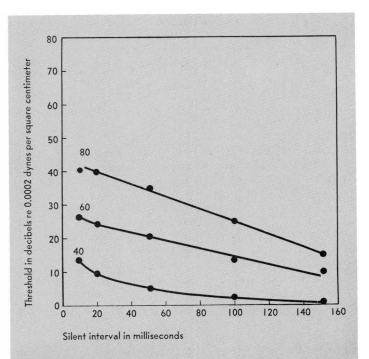

Figure 3-7. Auditory adaptation. Threshold intensity as a function of the time after the cessation of the adapting stimulus. The duration of the adaptation stimulus was 0.4 seconds; the numbers on each curve represent the intensity levels of the adapting stimulus. (E. Lüscher and Zwislocki. Acta oto-laryng, (Stockholm) 1947, 35, 428–445.)

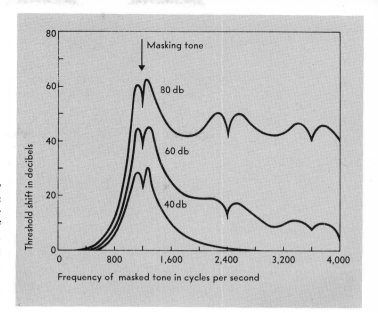

Figure 3-8. Auditory masking. The change in auditory threshold for various frequencies of the masked tone produced by a 1200-cps masking stimulus. (R.L. Wegel and C.E. Lane. Phys. Rev., 1924, 23, 266–285.)

the difference between these two thresholds as a measure of masking. These differences in threshold will be large for tones near the masking frequency and smaller for those tones farther away. An example of how this masking effect varies with the frequency of the test tone, when a 1200-cps masking tone is used, is shown in Figure 3-8. It is important to note two things about the curves here. The first is the general shape; there is more of a masking effect on tones higher than the masking tone than there is on lower tones. The second thing to note is the magnitude of the spread of the masking effect. There are appreciable effects several hundred cycles away from the masking tone. This illustrates the wide range of interaction of one tone with another and suggests that the auditory system is not sharply tuned. In many ways this suggestion is true, although we shall discuss in the next section some reasons for qualifying this statement. We might note in passing that when the masking effects spread over a region greater than one octave there are minor peaks of masking at the harmonics of the masking tone.

We can obtain results similar to those just described by employing more complex combinations of pure tones. For example, we can use a pair of pure tones, one on each side of the test tone whose threshold we wish to measure. We can then study the amount of masking we obtain as we move the masking tones away from the test tone. Again we find that we must move several hundred cycles away before the masking effect disappears. Similar results are obtained if we do our masking with noise that has been filtered in such a way that only certain frequency ranges are present in the noisy signal. If we arrange to center the range of frequencies in the noisy sound at the frequency of the test tone, we get a maximum masking effect. As long as the band of noise is not too wide, that is, as long as it does not extend over too broad a range of frequencies, all components of the noise contribute to the masking effect. When the noise band gets too wide, the noise components at the edges do not seem to contribute. Here, also, we find that we must make the band of frequencies several hundred cycles wide before we reach the point where increasing the width of the band of noise no longer has an effect on the threshold of the test stimulus.

Frequency Discrimination

There is one set of facts that does not seem to be consistent with this general picture that the auditory system is not sharply tuned. These facts come from the many observations on frequency discrimination. Suppose we present two tones in sequence and ask a subject whether he hears them as having a different pitch. If we vary the difference in the frequency of the two tones we can measure a threshold difference in frequency. The threshold we obtain turns out to depend on what our reference frequency is, that is, it depends on the frequency around which we vary the second tone to determine the threshold. The threshold frequency difference will also depend on the intensities of the tones. A typical set of measurements is shown in Figure 3-9. For frequencies below about 1000 cps, the threshold difference (Δf) is approximately constant at 2 or 3 cps. Above 1000 cps, the threshold frequency difference increases as we increase the reference frequency; it does so in such a way that the ratio of Δf to f is approximately a constant. All of the values for Δf in this graph are lowered by increasing the intensity of the tones and raised by decreasing the intensity of the tones.

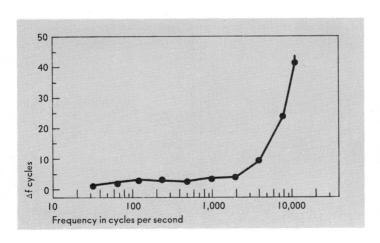

Figure 3-9. Auditor, frequency discrimination showing the threshold frequency difference as function of the frequency of the reference tone (Data from E.G. Showe and R. Biddulph. J acoust. Soc. Amer., 1931, 3, 275–287.)

One of the interesting things about these data on frequency discrimination is this: They suggest that the auditory system is about 20 to 50 times more sharply tuned than we might have expected from the masking data. We seem to have the capacity to allow broad interactions of frequency components as shown by the masking data, yet we are able to discriminate very small differences in frequency. We shall return to this problem when we discuss auditor mechanisms; at this point we leave it as an intriguing puzzle in auditor psychophysics.

The loudness of a sound
is usually correlated with the amplitude of the oscillation in pressure. If we increase the amplitude of the oscillation without changing its frequency, the subject will report that the tone becomes louder. One of the discriminations that is of interest in audition is our ability to detect changes in intensity. The results may be summarized in the following way: If the tone whose intensity we are going to change is initially loud, we need a smaller fractional, or percentage, change than if the tone is initially weak. At any given sound-pressure level, our ability to detect a change in intensity will depend on the frequency of the tone we are using. We are better at intermediate frequencies than we are at very high or very low frequencies.

These experiments on intensity discrimination and frequency discrimination present some theoretical difficulties, as did the experiment on exposure duration. We are studying stimuli that are varying in time, but we are trying to describe them in frequency terms. When we repeatedly switch from one frequency to another we introduce changes in the frequency spectrum that we might not expect from looking at the spectrum of each of the tones separately; we are actually doing something in this experiment that is familiar in radio engineering as frequency modulation. We cannot go into this problem in detail, but we can say that such a procedure yields a complicated spectrum. A similar situation develops when we systematically modify the peak amplitude of a sinusoidal wave. The case of a repetitive variation in the peak amplitude of a pure tone is called amplitude modulation. In both cases the theory for the spectral analysis of such signals is well developed, but the application of such theory to audition is complex.

THE NATURE OF PITCH PERCEPTION

We have noted that loudness is usually associated with the amplitude of the oscillation of our sound-generating source. Pitch is usually associated with the frequency of oscillation, that is, how rapidly the generating source moves to and fro. It is appropriate now to examine more closely the extent to which we can consider the ear as a frequency analyzer in dissecting out the frequency components of a complex wave. It is undoubtedly true that some kind of frequency analysis is performed in human hearing, and that pitch is related to frequency. However, it is misleading to leave the topic at that point. The human auditory system does some other things that are a little surprising. It seems to detect certain pitches when a frequency analysis would predict that these pitches should not be there. The case of the "missing fundamental" is a classic example of this. If we present a subject with a complex wave having frequency components of 2000, 2100, 2200, and 2300 cps, he will report hearing a pitch that is usually associated with a tone of 100 cps. This is the largest common denominator of the set of frequencies presented; all of the frequencies presented could be harmonics of 100 cps.

One of the early interpretations of this observation was that the auditory system introduced some distortion of the original stimulus. If this were true and if a frequency analysis were performed on the distorted signal, one would expect to find a frequency component at 100 cycles. While this interpretation persists, it encounters a number of difficulties. The first difficulty is that there is little evidence of distortion in the ear except at very high intensities. The second difficulty is that if the frequency of 100 cps were literally introduced into the auditory system, then it should be possible to treat it exactly like any other 100-cps tone we might put into the auditory system. For example, we should be able to mask it with noise. Yet if we take a noise band that contains all the frequencies below, say, 500 cycles so that the noise will mask a pure tone of 100 cps, but will not mask tones of 2000, 2100, 2200, and 2300 cps, we find that the missing fundamental is not masked.

Although the issue raised by the experiments on the "missing fundamental" is still not completely resolved, the results suggest that we have more than one pitch mechanism. Most of these phenomena—the missing fundamental, the effects of repeated burst of white noise, and so on—seem to occur primarily in a range below 1000 cps. In the high-frequency range, pitch is importantly a property of frequency in the physical sense of this term. In the lower range, we still respond accurately to pure tones, but we also assign a pitch quality to stimuli that may or may not have any frequency components in an appropriate range. The important physical feature of the stimuli that produce the pitch quality in the case of the missing fundamental is probably the envelope of the auditory signal. Another way of saying this is that we are sensitive to the over-all contour of the auditory signal as well as to some of the finer details. An example of what we mean by the envelope of a signal is shown in Figure 3-10.

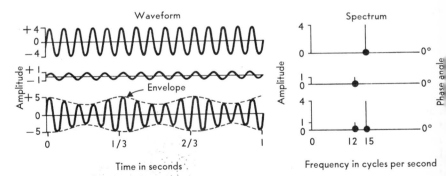

Figure 3-10. Schematic representation of an envelope produced by the mixing of two pure tones. (J.C.R. Licklider. In S.S. Stevens (ed.). Handbook of experimental psychology. New York: Wiley, 1951.)

If we take two frequencies shown in the spectrum to the right of the figure and mix them together we obtain a waveform that waxes and wanes in a simple manner shown by the dashed line. This line represents the envelope of the waveform. If we mix additional frequencies we can create more striking variations in the peaks and troughs of the resultant wave. This result should

Figure 3-11. Two wave-forms that can be gener-ated by mixing 30 fre-quencies. The difference between the top and bottom waveforms was produced by adjusting the relative phases of component frequencies. (W.A. van Bergeijk et al. Waves and the ear. New York: Doubleday, 1960.)

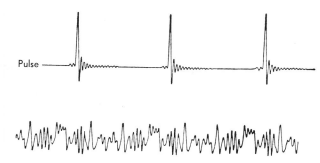

not surprise us because it is simply another version of what we have described as Fourier analysis and synthesis. We have already shown that we could generate a sawtooth wave by mixing together different sinusoidal frequencies. Our previous discussion did not adequately prepare us for one result, however: the importance of the phase of each of the component frequencies. We did say that we had to have information about phase in order to specify a sinusoid completely; in fact, the only difference between a sine wave and a cosine wave is that one is displaced in phase. Unfortunately, our synthesis of the sawtooth wave did not require that we manipulate the phase of any of the component frequencies; they all had the same phase. Although one frequently sees state-ments to the effect that the ear is not sensitive to phase, it now seems that the very essence of the "missing fundamental" phenomenon is the phase rela-tions of the component frequencies. This fact was highlighted a few years ago when one investigator reported that he could not obtain the missing funda-mental; his subjects did not report hearing anything that might be called the missing fundamental. It is now generally agreed that if the phases of the components used in a missing fundamental experiment are arranged randomly, the phenomenon disappears. The reason for this observation can be seen by examining Figure 3-11. This figure shows two waves, generated by exactly the same frequency components; the two waves differ only in the phase relations between the components. The sequence of pulses, if presented to the ear, would have a pitch quality equivalent to a sinusoid whose frequency corresponded to the repetition rate of the pulses as long as the repetition rate was not too high. Pulses of the sort shown in Figure 3-11, when repeated rapidly, will be heard as possessing pitch, provided that the repetition rate is greater than 20 and less than, say 500 or 600 times a second. Herein lies the basis for saying that we have two pitch mechanisms. We can only hear the missing funda-mental, or hear pitch when repeated bursts of noise are presented, if the envelope of the sound is going up and down at a rate less than, say, 1000 times a second. Above that value we only hear pitch if there is a distinctive frequency component present, in the sense that a Fourier analysis would show that we have the frequency present.

Physiological Mechanisms
in Audition

Figure 4-1 shows a diagramatic view of the major portions of the peripheral auditory system. We can divide this system into three parts: the external ear, the middle ear, and the inner ear. The tympanic membrane, or eardrum, separates the external ear from the middle ear, the oval window at the foot of the stapes separates the middle ear from the inner ear.

In examining the chain of events in auditory stimulation, we shall first describe these three major structures; after that we shall consider the activation of sense cells and nerve fibers of the auditory system.

58

4

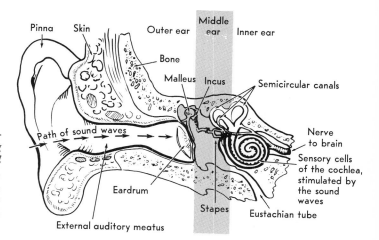

Figure 4-1. A cross section of the ear showing the outer, middle, and inner ear. (K. Davis. Hearing and deafness: a guide for laymen. New York: Murray Hill, 1947.)

Labels in figure:
Pinna | Skin | Outer ear | Middle ear | Inner ear
Bone
Malleus | Incus
Semicircular canals
Path of sound waves
Nerve to brain
Sensory cells of the cochlea, stimulated by the sound waves
Eardrum
Stapes
Eustachian tube
External auditory meatus

External Ear

The two major structures of the external ear are the pinna and the external auditory meatus. The pinna, although the most obvious part of the auditory system, probably does the least for audition. The structure and location of the pinna suggests that it serves as a sound reflector. It may serve this function for some animals; it probably does not do so in a significant way for man. The pinna may aid, to some extent, in the localization of sounds, particularly the discrimination between sounds in front and in back of us. The reason that the pinna is not an effective sound reflector in human audition is a simple physical one. For frequencies around 3000 cps and below, the wavelength of sound in air is larger than the pinna. This means that it will act to scatter the sound, rather than to reflect it in the technical sense.

The external auditory meatus is more important for human audition. This structure is a cylindrical cavity, approximately three centimeters in length, with an average diameter of seven millimeters. The cavity is open on the outside and bounded on the inside by the eardrum. This auditory canal, through which incoming pressure waves pass, contributes to our maximal sensitivity to tones around 2000 to 4000 cps. The air column filling this cavity has a resonant frequency of approximately 3000 cycles per second, resulting in a relative amplification at this frequency that is about ten times that for frequencies below 1000 cycles and above 7000 cycles.

We shall refer several times in this chapter to the *natural frequency* of various portions of the peripheral auditory system. This term comes from the analysis of physical and mechanical systems. It is a simple notion, in principle, although many of the applications become complicated. It is the principle that is involved in the tuning of a piano or a violin, or the adjustment of a clock. We know that a swing or a pendulum will, if displaced and released, oscillate at a certain rate depending on the length of the pendulum and its mass. A

Physiological Mechanisms in Audition

stretched system, such as piano or violin string will, if plucked, move to and fro at a rate that depends on its length and the tension under which it is held. The laws of mechanics allow us to determine the "preferred" frequencies of such systems. That such physical systems have certain "preferred" rates and modes of vibration does not mean, however, that they cannot be driven at other rates; indeed, they can be driven in almost any way we please if we have the power to do so. A pendulum that will swing freely at, say, one oscillation per second can be driven back and forth at a rate of ten or twenty oscillations a second. However, it is easier to drive such a system at its "natural" frequency than at any other. If what we try to make a system do corresponds to what the system "prefers" to do, we say that our input is matched to the system, that the system resonates to our driving stimulus.

Middle Ear

Pressure waves in the auditory meatus cause movements of the tympanic membrane and, thereby, set the middle-ear structures into motion. The middle-ear region is an air-filled cavity with a chain of three small bones linking the eardrum to the oval window of the inner ear. These bones, running in order from the eardrum to the oval window, are the malleus, the incus, and the stapes.

The middle ear plays an important role in determining the quantitative characteristics of auditory discrimination. There are several ways in which the structure of the middle ear influences the psychological data. The first is the contribution of the ear bones to our region of maximum sensitivity, for their natural frequency lies somewhere in the region of 2000 cps. A second is seen in what is called impedance matching in the ear. The tympanic membrane has an area of approximately one square centimeter, whereas the foot of the stapes has an area of approximately three square millimeters. This difference results in an increase in pressure in going from vibrations in air of the auditory canal to the fluids of the inner ear. This increase in pressure is a gain of approximately twenty times. Finally, the middle ear protects the inner ear from very intense sounds.

The middle-ear cavity is linked with the mouth cavity through the Eustachian tube. This arrangement permits the equalization of pressure on both sides of the tympanic membrane. Although steady pressures, or very slowly changing pressures, are not effective as auditory stimuli, steady differences in pressure between the middle ear and external ear do alter our sensitivity to different frequencies. We are probably all familiar with the alteration in the sounds we hear if we do not equalize the pressure changes resulting from ascending or descending in an elevator or an airplane.

Inner Ear

The next step in the chain of events in auditory stimulation is that the movement of the stapes exerts pressure on the fluid of the inner ear. The inner ear is a tubular structure, coiled on itself in a way that gives it the appearance of a snail shell. The number of coils varies from species to species; there are about three-and-one-half turns in the human ear, approximately four-and-one-half turns in the ear of the guinea pig. The inner ear is filled with fluid and is partitioned into two regions, the scala vestibuli and the scala tympani, by a structure called the cochlear partition. The sequence of events that follow a movement of the middle-ear bones involves the displacement of several structures. An inward movement of the foot of the stapes at the oval window moves the fluid of the upper chamber of the inner ear, the scala vestibuli. Since this fluid is essentially incompressible, the cochlear partition is forced downward against the fluid in the lower chamber of the inner ear. Since this fluid is also incompressible, the movement of the cochlear partition results in an outward movement of the flexible round window. These movements are reversed when the pressure wave moves the stapes in the opposite direction.

THE ACTION OF THE COCHLEAR PARTITION

Some aspect of this repetitive movement of the cochlear partition is what activates the sense cells and their associated nerve fibers. Thus, it becomes important to know exactly what the vibration pattern of the cochlear partition is. Historically, much of the uncertainty about how we achieve the fine auditory discriminations discussed in the previous chapter centered on the many and diverse views of what the cochlear partition did when sound waves were presented to the ear. These various theories of how the ear worked fell into two broad classes, (1) frequency theories and (2) place theories. In general, the frequency theories supposed that the basilar membrane, the structure in the cochlear partition containing the sense cells, vibrated more or less uniformly and followed the waveform of the stimulus, much like the diaphragm of a microphone. The place theories assumed that the inner ear was constructed in such a way that different regions of the basilar membrane vibrated when different frequencies were used. Although auditory theories did not clearly fall into one of these two categories, the differences between place and frequency theories highlighted the uncertainty about what the cochlear partition did when stimulated; the exact form that auditory theories took depended on the assumptions that were made about the physical properties of the inner ear.

The differences in the interpretation of how the ear worked were not easy to resolve by experiment because of the small size of the inner ear structures and because of their general inaccessibility. The length of the cochlear partition is less than one-and-one-half inches (about 35 millimeters). Experimentation was difficult because this structure was coiled and, in addition, was surrounded by bony structures. It was not until the ingenious experimental work of von Bekesy, beginning in the 1920's, that we began to acquire the kind of information we need to describe how the inner ear works. Bekesy was able to observe the movements of the cochlear partition by cutting several holes in the wall of this coiled tube and inserting windows in these regions to permit the observation of movements of the cochlear partition with a microscope. A little thought will, of course, lead us to question how these movements can be observed, if the partition is moving up and down many hundreds of times per second. We have already seen in our study of critical fusion frequency that the eye is not equipped to follow such rapid alternations. Bekesy solved this problem by using a rapidly pulsating light to illuminate the vibrating structure; he synchronized the flash rate of this light source with the oscillations of the auditory stimulus. The principle used here is a simple one frequently used in demonstrations in elementary science. He utilized a stroboscopic phenomenon. For example, it is possible to make a rotating fan appear to stop if the blades of the fan are illuminated at the same rate as the rate of their rotation. If the illuminating light flashes at the same rate as the fan is spinning, the blades are always illuminated when they are in a particular position, and they appear to stand still. Bekesy used an analogous technique to measure the vibration pattern of the cochlear partition.

The results of Bekesy's observations showed that the basal end of the partition, that is, the region of the partition near the stapes, vibrated more when high frequencies were used as stimuli. The apical end, the part of the cochlear partition farthest away from the stapes, vibrated more when low frequencies were used. It was clear from these observations that the general expectations of the place theories were supported. The region of maximum vibration varies systematically with the frequency of the stimulus. Examples of the vibration pattern exhibited by the cochlear partition for each of four stimulus frequencies are shown in Figure 4-2.

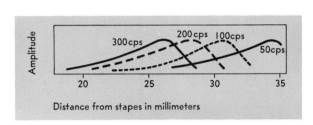

Figure 4-2. The amplitude and locus of vibration of the cochlear partition when the ear is presented with pure tones of 300, 200, 100, and 50 cps. (G. von Bekesy and W.A. Rosenblith. In S.S. Stevens. Ibid.)

There are two noteworthy aspects of the results presented by Bekesy. We have already referred to the first of these, that there is a difference in the vibration pattern of the cochlear partition for different frequencies of auditory stimuli. The general features of a place theory thus seem to be correct. Additional measurements by Bekesy dealt with the phase relations between the stimulus and the vibration of the cochlear partition and with the extent to which the structures of this partition are under tension. This spatial localization is now felt to be a consequence of the hydrodynamics of the fluids in the inner ear and the general stiffness of the structures of the cochlear partition.

Although this experiment clearly shows that the frequency of the stimulus is translated into a position of peak activity along the cochlear partition, it also shows a second noteworthy result, that the effects of a single pure tone are widespread. The observations on the movement of the cochlear partition seem to be in harmony with our earlier observations on masking. There we found modifications in the thresholds for pure tones that spread several hundred cycles away from the frequency of a masking tone. This broad interaction of frequencies is what we would expect from the vibration patterns reported by Bekesy. These broad vibration patterns pose the same question that we encountered earlier in discussing the masking data. If the system is that broadly tuned to frequency, how can we detect small differences in frequency?

There are probably many ways in which this kind of sharpening in the frequency analysis could be achieved, but let us look at one that is known to be involved. To see its operation we must look more carefully at the sensory apparatus and its nerve supply. Figure 4-3 shows a schematic view of the cochlear partition and some of its component structures. Of particular interest to us are the hair cells and their associated nerve fibers. The hair cells are arranged in two sets, the inner and the outer hair cells. When the sense cells in a given region of the basilar membrane are activated, nerve fibers from this region are stimulated. The fibers serving the hair cells group together to form the auditory nerve. These fibers are bipolar cells, with one extension running to the sense cell area within the cochlear partition, the other extension running in the auditory nerve and ending in the central nervous system. They enter the central nervous system in the lower part of the brain, an area called the medulla; they terminate in a region of the medulla called the cochlear nucleus. From this cochlear nucleus the auditory messages are sent to the inferior colliculus, then to the medial geniculate body, and finally to the auditory cortex in the temporal lobe of the brain.

What kind of responses do we record at the various way-stations in the auditory system? Let us begin with nerve fibers in the auditory nerve. The auditory nerve fibers are first-order neurons. Imagine that we are recording from a fiber that arose from some point along the basilar membrane whose peak excursion occurs when stimulated by a tone of 500 cps. From what we

Figure 4-3. A cross section through the cochlear partition showing the auditory sense cells (inner and outer hair cells). (A.T. Rasmussen. Outlines of neuro-anatomy. *Dubuque, Iowa: Brown, 1943.)*

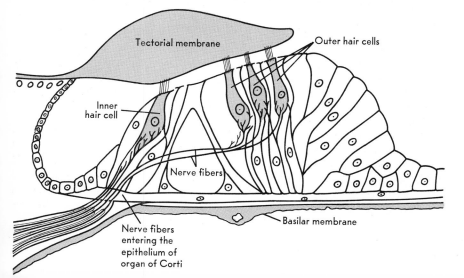

have seen of the vibration patterns in the cochlea, this region is likely to be stimulated to some extent by all frequencies below 500 cps and by many frequencies above this. We expect that the cut-off for high frequencies will be sharper than that observed for low frequencies. In fact, this is what we find; each nerve fiber will be stimulated by a wide range of frequencies.

The easiest way to show the nature of the response in the auditory system is to plot what is called a response area; this is a graph of the combinations of different intensities and frequencies of tones that will elicit a response in a given nerve fiber. To measure such a response area we begin by selecting a stimulus of weak intensity and varying the frequency of this stimulus until we have sampled the full audible range. If we observe no response to any of these stimuli we increase the intensity and scan, once again, through the audible range of frequencies. We continue this procedure until we observe a response. When we find an intensity that will just give us some response, we observe that we obtain this response only over a very narrow band of frequencies, perhaps five or ten cycles. The intensity that will just give us a response at some frequency is called the threshold intensity; the center of the band of frequencies that are effective at this threshold intensity is called the characteristic frequency of the fiber. If we now continue to increase the intensity above the threshold level and test for the nerve response at various frequencies, we find that the band of effective frequencies gradually increases; at very high intensities it may cover many hundreds of cycles. A curve drawn around all of the intensities and frequencies that will be effective in stimulating a nerve fiber in the auditory system defines the response area. Curve *a* in Figure 4-4 is an example of such a response area for one nerve fiber.

Even though the band of effective frequencies broadens as we increase the intensity of the stimulus, it is still true that an individual nerve cell retains a certain preference for the characteristic frequency. It does so by giving a greater response, that is, a greater number of impulses or a higher rate of discharge, at or near the characteristic frequency.

If we were to record from another nerve fiber we might find that its characteristic frequency was 2000 cps, rather than 500 cps, and it would have its own threshold intensity and therefore its own particular response area. Individual fibers will differ from one another in the numerical value of their characteristic frequency, their threshold intensity, and therefore their response area.

These results show us that individual fibers are tuned to a limited band of frequencies and they maintain a certain degree of sharpness of tuning, even at high intensities, by virtue of the magnitude of the response they give to test stimuli. It is difficult to imagine, however, that this mechanism in the auditory nerve could yield the fine frequency discrimination of two or three cycles that is so typical of the psychophysical data. Some other mechanism must be operating in the auditory system to give us fine discrimination. Let us now repeat the experiment just described, but with one modification; let us record from single nerve fibers in the various auditory centers. This leads to an interesting result. Each nerve cell in any of these centers has its own response area, but we find that the response area is narrower for cells in the higher centers than for cells in lower centers. A cell in the medial geniculate

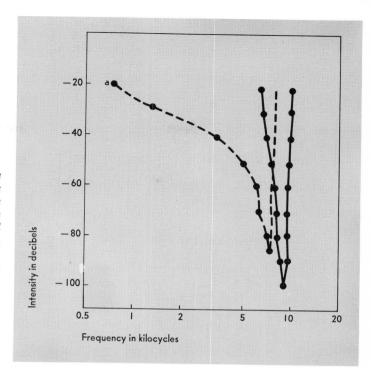

Figure 4-4. Response areas of single neurons in the auditory nerve (broken line) and in the inferior colliculus (solid line). The response area includes all intensity-frequency combinations to which the single neuron will respond. (Y. Katsuki. In W.A. Rosenblith (ed.). Sensory communications. Cambridge: MIT Press, and New York: Wiley, 1961.)

body, for example, exhibits a narrower response area than a cell in the cochlear nucleus. This sharpening of the response areas is illustrated in Figure 4-4.

It is not certain exactly how this sharpening occurs. We have seen an example of an inhibitory mechanism in the visual system, a mechanism that probably operates in simultaneous contrast and serves to enhance the contours or edges of visual figures. Perhaps an analogous mechanism is operating in the auditory system.

One of the important, and perhaps unexpected, results of the many studies that have been performed on single nerve cells in the auditory system is the observation that cells with characteristic frequencies below 200 or 300 cycles per second are rarely found. It seems as if there are no fibers that are specially tuned to the low frequencies. Below 200–300 cps, however, another phenomena appears that is undoubtedly of significance in our interpretation of pitch perception. If we use a low-frequency tone (say 50 cps) and find a fiber that responds to it, even though the characteristic frequency of the fiber is higher than 50 cps, we observe that the impulses seem to be paced by the oscillations of pressure. More careful examination reveals that the impulses are initiated at a certain point in the oscillation of the cochlear partition. The nerve is excited when the basilar membrane is moving upward into the scala vestibuli. This is equivalent to saying that nerve fiber is stimulated when the stapes moves outward from the inner ear. Increasing the intensity of the stimulus at these low frequencies will increase the number of impulses we observe, but these impulses will still remain grouped. With an intensity somewhat above threshold we may get two or three impulses for every one we had recorded with a weaker intensity, but the impulses now occur in pairs or triplets; these sets of two or three impulses also appear to be triggered at about the same point in the waveform of the stimulus. If we record from a large number of fibers simultaneously, we get massive firing of the many nerve fibers, but the total amount of firing still tends to wax and wane at a rate that corresponds to the frequency of the tone used. Such results remind us of a frequency type of interpretation of hearing. The rate of waxing and waning of activity in the auditory nerve corresponds to the frequency of the stimulus; this oscillation could provide a mechanism for pitch discrimination.

The important point to note about the pacing of responses in single nerve fibers is that this tendency for impulses to "follow" the waveform of the stimulus fails at high frequencies. This failure is due partly to the inability of any nerve fiber to follow extremely rapid stimulation, for there is a physiological limit to the rate of firing of any nerve fiber. This failure also results from an intrinsic variability in the nerve response. The impulses may be initiated at the same point in the waveform, but repetitive measurements of the time interval between a stimulus and the first impulse response demonstrate that this interval is not always the same. All of the impulses *tend* to occur at the same point. What actually happens is that the impulses cluster around a point in the waveform; they do not always occur at exactly the same point in the waveform. This variability becomes important at high frequencies. It obscures the pacing that is intrinsic in the mechanism and gives the impression that the impulses are more or less randomly placed with respect to the waveform. Because of this variability the pacing or grouping of impulses begins to disappear at about 1000 cycles per second. Above this frequency of 1000 cps we must discriminate pitch by some type of place mechanism, that is, on the basis of which fibers are active; below this frequency we may discriminate pitch on the basis of the waxing and waning of activity in many nerve fibers.

Taste

We have repeatedly emphasized that one of the major concerns of sensory psychology has been, and continues to be, the problem of discovering an appropriate descriptive language. This problem appears with no greater force than in the areas of taste and olfaction. For these senses, the stimuli are likely to be complex molecules, and the attempt to study the way in which these molecules affect the sense cells takes us into the areas of physical and biological chemistry. In some cases, we are drawn to the frontiers of physiological chemistry in our search for useful ideas about how the taste and olfactory systems work.

5

In taste, as in other branches of sensory psychology, the starting point for our study is the systematic observation of what man can discriminate. Unfortunately, what we refer to as taste in everyday conversation is, in fact, a mixture of several modalities. When we speak of the taste of coffee or bananas, we are really including smell and touch as well as taste. Many substances that we consider to have distinctively different tastes, such as coffee and quinine, would be difficult to discriminate without their associated odors. Because of this common interaction it is important in experimental work on either modality to control for this confusion.

Primary Tastes

Much of the early history of sensory psychology was devoted to a careful reporting by trained observers of the basic qualities in each of the sense modalities. We see the consequences of these observations for the sense of taste in the four-fold classification of sweet, bitter, salt, and sour. Some authors have suggested a fifth or sixth basic taste, but most experimenters still adhere to the four-way classification. Such classification procedures have had as one of their objectives the identification of the primary sensory events out of which the responses to complex stimuli are built. We have seen these procedures at work in the case of color vision with the gradual development of formulations that assume three or four primary color mechanisms and postulate that our responses to complex colored stimuli are built up out of the interactions of these basic processes. The identification of such primary processes is not easy to achieve and it is not likely to result, as was once thought, from the gradual agreement in what trained observers say. Such verbal reports are interesting and important and they provide helpful guidelines for our thinking; but the classifications they lead to must eventually be consistent with many other kinds of data. We have also seen this evolutionary process operating in the field of color vision. Any acceptable notion of color vision must allow us to account for such diverse observations as the mixing of colors, color blindness, and wavelength discrimination. We must expect and demand as much in the investigation of taste.

Most observers will agree that substances such as salt, quinine, sugar, and lemon juice taste different. We use the labels salty, bitter, sweet, and sour to describe these substances. Our experience and language suggest that these tastes are qualitatively different, that is, one taste does not seem to be simply a more intense version of the taste of another.

What other kinds of evidence do we have to support the use of these four tastes as primaries? One kind of evidence comes from the regional sensitivities of the tongue. If we measure the threshold for quinine and for sugar at various parts of the tongue, we find that the tip of the tongue is more sensitive to sugar than is the base, whereas the back of the tongue is more sensitive to quinine than is the tip. Similar determinations for the salt and sour tastes show that sensitivity to salt is greatest on the tip and sides of the tongue and sensitivity to sour is greatest on the sides. Although there is considerable overlap in these maps of regional sensitivity for the four taste stimuli, it is quite clear that the regions are not identical.

Another kind of evidence for the separation of these four taste qualities comes from observations on the effects of drugs on taste sensitivity. A drug like gymnemic acid seems to have no effect on the threshold for sour and salty substances, but reduces our sensitivity to sweet and bitter substances. The drug cocaine has a quantitatively different effect on all four tastes. It greatly reduces our sensitivity to bitter; it has the least effect on sensitivity to salt; it has intermediate effects on sweet and sour, affecting sweet more than sour. Similar separations of these taste qualities are found in the recovery of taste sensitivity following anesthesia.

A third line of evidence comes from attempts to stimulate individual taste buds. Most buds are found to be sensitive to all four of the taste stimuli, but some respond only to salt, others only to sweet, and still others only to sour. A number of other kinds of evidence could be outlined to strengthen the position that our taste discriminations are based on the activation of a number of primary systems and that the interactions of these primary systems are involved in complex tastes.

The next question we might ask is, "What is the evidence that there are just four primary systems rather than, say, 50 of them?" For example, we have talked rather loosely about the "salt" taste and salt stimuli. Usually the material used experimentally is common table salt, sodium chloride. However, this is just one of a large class of materials that the chemist calls salt, all of which do not taste alike. The negatively charged chlorine ion in the expression $NaCl$ can be replaced by the radical (SO_4) to form a sulphate salt; the positive ion, sodium, can be replaced by other metallic ions, such as potassium and calcium, to form other chloride or sulphate salts.

If we have a subject compare sodium chloride and potassium chloride, he will say that they have different tastes. Among the materials the chemist calls salts, sodium chloride seems to be the only one that gives a "pure" salt taste. Potassium chloride, for instance, is salty, but it is also slightly bitter and sour. It is both interesting and important that one can, indeed, mix a combination of a salt substance (sodium chloride), a bitter substance (such as quinine), and a sour substance (such as an acid) in such a way that the combination tastes like potassium chloride. This is analogous to the mixing of red-, green-, and blue-colored stimuli and reproducing all of the spectral colors. We do not have as much data on taste mixing as we do on color mixtures, but at least one detailed experiment has shown us the relative proportions of four basic taste stimuli required to match a long series of salt compounds. It is this kind of result that convinces us of the usefulness of such a four-way classification.

If we accept, provisionally, the notion that we have a small number of primary taste systems, the next problem that we must investigate is what critical aspects of different stimuli initiate these tastes. We have already seen that sodium chloride is a principal source of the salt taste, that it is, perhaps, the only substance that yields a "pure" salt taste. Yet, we also know that materials containing neither sodium nor chlorine taste salty. It seems as if this sensitivity is some type of ion sensitivity. The most common stimuli used for the sour taste are the acids, particularly acids of low molecular weight. Acids have the property of releasing hydrogen ions in water, and this seems to be an important condition for the sensation of sourness. Therefore, the sour taste also seems to involve some kind of ion sensitivity. An inspection of sweet and bitter substances shows the greatest diversity of stimuli, as far as chemical structure is concerned. The sugars are particularly efficient producers of the sweet taste; generally speaking, the carbohydrates, of which the sugars are one class, taste sweet. Typical stimuli for the bitter taste are the alkaloids, quinine and caffeine being examples in this category.

These approximate descriptions of the classes of stimuli that elicit each of the primary tastes are, at best, incomplete. There exists no descriptive system that can characterize these primaries without an extended list of exceptions. Many of the heavy metallic salts—for example, lead salts such as lead acetate—taste sweet. In fact, lead acetate is frequently referred to as "sugar of lead" by the chemist. Although the acids usually taste sour, the amino acids tend to taste sweet, while picric acid is bitter. Some of the sweetest-tasting materials—for example, saccharin and dulcin—have chemical structures quite different from the sugars. Saccharin is approximately 500 times as effective in eliciting a report of sweet as is the commonly used sugar, sucrose.

Fortunately, we need not have a completely adequate description of the critical stimuli for these tastes before we can study other aspects of our response to taste stimuli. On the contrary, it may be through the study of other phenomena, such as selective adaptation or masking, that we will acquire new insights into the problem of grouping taste stimuli.

Adaptation and Contrast

Taste thresholds depend importantly on the level of adaptation of the sensory system. If we expose the tongue to salt for a period of time, we gradually decrease our sensitivity to salt. This change in threshold occurs rapidly at first and then more slowly. We approach a new stable threshold after several minutes of adaptation. The amount and the rate of change in threshold depend on the concentration of salt to which we adapt; the threshold undergoes more extensive changes when we adapt to high concentrations of salt than when we adapt to low concentrations. An example of the experimental measurements of this phenomenon is shown in Figure 5-1.

This change in threshold during adaptation is a reversible process, and we can show the recovery to our original sensitivity by removing the adapting stimulus and measuring the threshold as a function of time. Figure 5-1 also shows this recovery from three different concentrations of adapting stimuli. Comparable curves of adaptation and recovery may be obtained using other taste stimuli.

We can extend this adaptation experiment by measuring the effect that adaptation to one substance has on the thresholds for other taste materials. Some of these effects of cross-adaptation are complex. We might expect that any adapting stimulus that activates, say, the sour system will have an effect on other sour-tasting stimuli. In general, this is true of the weak acids; if we adapt the tongue to one acid, we typically change the threshold for other acids. The picture is less clear, however, when we study the other taste qualities.

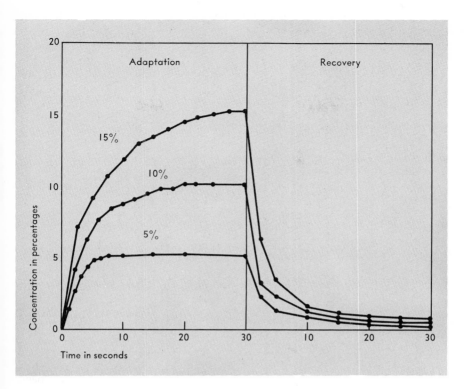

Figure 5-1. Adaptation and recovery curves for sodium chloride concentrations of 5, 10, and 15 per cent. Thresholds are given in percentages of concentration. Adaptation and recovery periods are of 30 seconds duration. (C. Pfaffmann. In S.S. Stevens (ed.). Handbook of experimental psychology. *New York: Wiley, 1951.)*

There are also a number of after-effects of stimulation that seem to be related to these adaptation phenomena. Stimulation with a weak acid will normally produce a sour taste. It also does something else; immediately afterwards, distilled water will taste sweet. This is a type of successive contrast that is encountered in other sensory areas. In addition to successive contrast, it is possible to measure a phenomenon of simultaneous contrast in taste. If we stimulate one side of the tongue with a weak acid or a sugar, we lower the threshold for salt on the other side of the tongue. This enhancement of sensitivity occurs only if the adapting stimulus is weak, however. Strong solutions will cause an *increase* in the salt threshold on the opposite side of the tongue. This instance provides a good example of the necessity of investigating many values of stimulus intensity in any experiment in sensory psychology. If this experiment had been performed using just one concentration of sugar, we could have been led to any one of three conclusions. We might have observed an enhancing effect, an inhibitory effect, or no effect at all, depending on the value of concentration selected. Any one of these conclusions would have been correct for that concentration, but the likelihood of making a faulty generalization from the results would have been great.

The Effect of Area, Exposure Duration, and Temperature

Three other variables that influence taste thresholds are the size of the stimulated area, the duration of the stimulus exposure, and the temperature of the solution used. We have already stated that, if we restrict the area stimulated to single papillae, some will respond only to one of the classes of taste. This is one extreme of the experimental problem of the dependence of taste thresholds on the size of the stimulus. In general, for all of the taste qualities, there is an inverse relation between the size of the stimulated area and the threshold concentration; the larger the area, the lower the threshold concentration. The relations between threshold concentration and the length of time a stimulus is presented is also an inverse one.

In describing these relations we must, again, be careful of the units of measurement we use when we summarize the results. The inverse relationship between threshold and exposure time, for example, is true when we use concentration as the measure of stimulus intensity. But if we are interested in the number of molecules that are required to activate the taste system at threshold, we find that the number increases with increasing exposure time.

The effect of the temperature of the solution on our threshold determinations is a complex one, since it depends on the stimulus substance used. Temperature seems to be a relatively unimportant variable when we are measuring thresholds for sour substances, such as hydrochloric acid. When we use sodium chloride, however, there is a linear increase in threshold as we increase the temperature of the solution. A more complex relationship is found with the bitter and sweet substances. The evidence suggests that the threshold for sweet stimuli decreases and then increases as we increase the temperature of the solution. An adequate interpretation of these complex effects of temperature is not yet available, but these data suggest that the mechanisms for tasting these different materials may be quite different.

Variability of Taste Thresholds

If we measure the thresholds for a large number of materials using a large number of subjects, several points become obvious. The first is that there are substantial differences among individuals in the thresholds for given substances; the second is that all substances do not yield the same amount of variability. Some taste stimuli show very small differences in threshold from one individual to another—everyone has about the same threshold for the particular taste stimulus. Saccharine and picric acid are examples of such stimuli. Other substances, such as vanillin and phenylthiocarbamide, show very large differences among individuals. If we plot frequency distributions for the thresholds for different taste stimuli, we observe that most of the stimuli yield single-humped distributions. Stated another way, for most stimuli there is a most common threshold value and fewer and fewer individuals have thresholds as we move below or above this modal value. Examples of some of these distributions are shown in Figure 5-2. A few substances (phenylthiocarbamide, or PTC, is one of these) show frequency distributions that have two peaks. If we take PTC as an example, we find that some persons are very sensitive, others are very insensitive to this substance, and very few individuals have thresholds between these extremes. The individuals falling into the two major portions of such a frequency distribution are sometimes called "tasters" and "nontasters," respectively. The fact that the thresholds for PTC are quite reliable and consistent within an individual suggests that we have here a demonstration of "taste blindness" analogous to color blindness in vision. Perhaps "taste weakness" would be a more appropriate label, since all subjects are able to taste this substance if the concentration is high enough.

For many taste stimuli there are also large differences in threshold for a person from time to time. There is evidence that thresholds are different at different times of the day; some of these variations may be related to our eating habits. Taste thresholds for sugar, for instance, depend on the level of sugar in the blood. Changes in hormone secretion are also known to change taste preferences, both in lower animals and in man. Not only do such internal factors influence the thresholds and preferences for taste stimuli, but the injection of certain drugs into the circulatory system leads to a report of taste

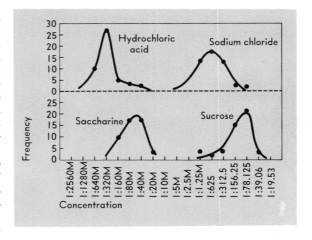

Figure 5-2. (A) The variability in taste thresholds for various substances. Forty-seven individuals were tested on each substance; the ordinate gives the number of persons (frequency) showing thresholds at the concentrations indicated on the abscissa. The concentrations give the ratio of dilution (M = x1000), with each successive concentration being just double the preceding one. (A.T. Blakeslee and T.H. Salman. Proc. nat. Acad. Sci., 1935, 21, 84–90.) (B) The variability in thresholds for bitter-tasting phenyl-thiocarbamide (PTC). Note the two distinct peaks which separate the population into "tasters" and "nontasters" for this substance. (W. Setterfield, R.G. Shatt, S.K. Snyder. Ohio J. Sci., 1936, 36, 231–235.)

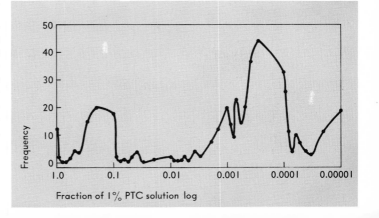

even when no taste stimulus is applied to the tongue. In this regard the taste system is probably more intimately tied to the internal environment of the organism than is any other sensory system.

The first stage of our sensory system for taste consists of sets of cells called taste buds. Each taste bud is a cluster of from two to twelve separate cells. These taste buds range in size from about 30 μ to about 110 μ. In human beings the taste buds are approximately 50 μ in length and about 40 μ in width. Several nerve fibers enter each taste bud, and an individual nerve fiber may go to more than one taste bud. These nerve fibers group together and travel in one of three cranial nerves, the VII (or facial) nerve, the IX (or glossopharyngeal) nerve, or the X (or vagus) nerve. There is a specialization of function in these nerve bundles. Thus, the VIIth nerve services the anterior two-thirds of the tongue, the IXth nerve innervates the posterior one-third of the tongue, the Xth nerve carries information about taste from the pharynx.

These three cranial nerves also perform functions other than delivering information about taste stimuli; they are mixed nerves in the sense that they contain both motor and sensory nerve fibers. They transmit information from the central nervous system to the muscles of the face and tongue; they also carry information to the central nervous system from many types of sense cells. The sensory part of these bundles is, itself, mixed, for it contains fibers serving the tactile and temperature senses, as well as those serving taste.

The sensory fibers coming from the taste buds run to the nuclei of their respective cranial nerves. These nuclei are located in the lower part of the brain in a region called the medulla. From these nuclei the information goes to specific regions in the thalamus and, subsequently, to the regions in the cortex of the brain. In both the thalamus and the brain the taste regions lie adjacent to, and probably overlap with, the areas serving the touch sense for the face.

The senses of taste and smell are sometimes discussed together under the broader heading of the chemical senses. It is reasonable to suppose that the way in which taste stimuli initiate activity in the sensory system involves some kind of chemical interaction between the taste substance and some chemical or physical feature of the sense cell. What must concern us is the kind of chemical interaction involved. We have already seen one kind of chemical reaction in the study of vision: a photochemical reaction. In this case light bombards complex molecules in the visual sense cells and this energy bombardment changes the molecule, rhodopsin, into another substance. This sequence of chemical changes leads to the activation of the sense cell, which in turn initiates nerve activity. In the case of taste we are dealing with a different kind of chemical system and the question is "What kind of a system is it?" Several suggestions have been made to explain how chemicals that serve as taste stimuli alter the state of the taste sense cell. One suggestion is that the activation of the taste cell involves some process of adsorption, some adhesive action between the taste molecule and the sense cell surface. Another suggestion involves the notion of enzyme activity. Enzymes are organic, or biological, catalysts; a catalyst is a substance that affects the speed of a chemical reaction without, itself, entering into the formula for the chemical reaction. The attractiveness of this notion derives partly from some of the properties of enzyme systems. Biological enzyme systems differ in some important ways from many inorganic catalysts. For one thing, their action is frequently extremely specific; enzymes may influence only one or a small number of chemical reactions. It has been suggested that one of the reasons for this specificity of action is that the way in which enzymes influence chemical reactions depends on the structural arrangement of the atoms. This interpretation of enzyme activity is sometimes called the "lock-and-key theory." It implies that the enzyme must in some way be able to "lock in" to the molecular structure of one of the components in the chemical reaction.

In addition to the specificity exhibited by many enzyme systems, they also seem to be more specifically dependent on such variables as temperature and pH (a measure of acidity and alkalinity) for their effectiveness. Some of these characteristics of enzyme systems correspond to the observations of taste sensitivity.

The enzyme theory encounters a number of difficulties, however. If an enzyme action is involved in the activation of the taste system, it must be an enzyme system that is different from the common systems known to exist; many substances that inhibit the action of known enzyme systems do not alter taste thresholds. Nevertheless, the subject of enzyme action is a rapidly changing one in biological chemistry and future research may uncover specialized systems in taste. Recently two enzymes that are inhibited by certain taste stimuli have been found in the taste buds of lower animals. One of these enzymes is inhibited by vanillin but is unaffected by salt, sugar, and quinine; the other enzyme is inhibited by quinine but not by salt and sugar.

Whatever the nature of the initial changes induced by taste stimuli, the latter must eventually change the state of the sense cell in a way that will activate sensory nerve fibers. One of the earliest studies of the activity of single nerve fibers of the taste system was performed by Carl Pfaffmann. He showed that individual fibers are specialized in the way they respond. Some taste fibers respond only to acid, or sour, stimuli. Other fibers respond to acid and quinine. A third group of fibers respond to acid and to salt. Therefore, all fibers respond to acid. Pfaffmann found no fibers sensitive to stimulation by sugar. Of course, it is always difficult to conclude from such a result that there are no fibers that respond to sugar; such fibers may exist but may simply be located in such a place or respond in such a way that the experimental procedure did not uncover them. Indeed, subsequent research has shown that some nerve fibers respond to sugar. This result serves as a reminder that we must always be concerned with the possible limitations of any experimental procedure, and, no less so in the physiological case, we must be aware of what we can and cannot do—and, therefore, what we can and cannot conclude. In addition to this concern we must be constantly alert to the possible differences among species, since most of the physiological work is done on lower animals. As an example, we might note that some species apparently have specialized water receptors, for some fibers will give a response to distilled water. The few attempts to record from single nerve fibers in the human taste system indicate that we have no specialized water receptors. This finding is consistent with the fact that we do not say that water has a distinctive taste. The water we drink may have a taste, if it has a high mineral content or has been heavily chlorinated; distilled water, however, lacks distinctive taste qualities. Another example of these differences among species may be seen in the relative responsiveness to different salts. Some animals, such as the rat and the guinea pig, give a greater response to sodium chloride than they do to potassium chloride, whereas other animals, such as the dog and cat, show greater sensitivity to potassium chloride.

All the physiological work on single nerve cells points to the conclusion that the primary taste qualities isolated by introspective analysis must result from a patterning of activity in a number of nerve fibers. We have mentioned that the neural innervation of the taste cells is such that individual taste cells receive branches from more than one nerve fiber and one nerve fiber sends branches to more than one taste cell. The possibility exists that the individual taste cells respond more specifically than do the nerve fibers. The best available evidence suggests that this is not true, however. When very small electrodes are placed in individual taste cells we obtain results similar to those described in the case of the individual nerve fibers.

Many other behavioral phenomena described in the earlier portions of this chapter have their counterpart in the physiological data. For example, single nerve cells exhibit the phenomenon of successive contrast. We can initiate activity in a given nerve cell, using stimuli that are not typically effective for that cell, by presenting such stimuli after the presentation of a different stimulus. A fiber that may respond to sugar and not respond to distilled water will, after being stimulated with a weak acid (sour), respond to water. This result is consistent with our earlier statement that the human observer reports that water tastes sweet if it is presented immediately after a weak acid that tastes sour.

Such results raise some interesting questions concerning the isolation of the sensitivities of individual nerve cells. They demand that the sensitivity of individual fibers be determined only under conditions that eliminate these subtle effects of prior stimulation.

Smell

Because the sensory apparatus in olfaction is so inaccessible, one of the difficulties faced by the experimenter is the problem of devising reliable techniques for presenting stimuli to the subject. In everyday experience we usually sniff to accentuate the olfactory cues in the environment. This procedure is also used frequently in the laboratory. You may readily appreciate that it is difficult to standardize what is meant by a "sniff"; nevertheless, usable results can be obtained with this method. The "sniff" technique demands that we make careful arrangements for quantifying the amount of odorous material available.

77

6

Techniques for Measuring Olfactory Thresholds

One method of making careful measurements is to use an instrument called an olfactometer. Usually this apparatus is a copy of, or a modification of, a design proposed by Zwaardemaker, one of the early research workers in olfaction. It consists of a pair of concentric tubes, one of which slides inside the other, like the arm of a slide trombone. The inner surface of the outer tube is coated with the odorous material so that if we slide one of these tubes with respect to the other we change the amount of surface of odorous material over which air travels. One end of the inner tube is led to the nostril, so that a sniff will cause air to pass over the material on its way to the nasal cavity. Although this seems like a crude method, reliable results can be obtained if care is taken to control for the temperature, the humidity, and the purity of the air. Particular attention must also be paid to the purity of the odorous material used, because of the great sensitivity of the olfactory system.

A second procedure that attempts to eliminate some of the uncertainties of the sniff is called the "blast-injection" technique. With this method the volume of the gas, the pressure with which the gas is applied, and the duration of the exposure can be controlled by the experimenter. A subject smells passively when this procedure is used; he is instructed to hold his breath while the stimulus is presented.

Differences in experimental procedures for measuring thresholds lead to large differences in the statements about olfactory sensitivity. Sensitivity measurements may vary by a factor of 100 depending on the method used. Generally, however, the relative standings of the threshold for different materials are not markedly changed with the method of measurement.

Primary Odors

In olfaction, as in taste, an attempt has been made to analyze the many different odors we can discriminate and to represent them as combinations of a small number of primary odors. There is still no general agreement that any one of the classifications of primary systems proposed in the past is satisfactory in organizing the data of olfaction. One of the earliest schemes was suggested by Linnaeus, the botanist to whom we are indebted for the early classification of the plant kingdom. He listed the seven primary odors given in Table 6-1. Another classification of historical interest is that offered by Zwaardemaker. The set of fundamental smells most frequently referred to, however, is one proposed by Henning. This scheme provided a six-way classification with the labels shown in Table 6-1. A more recent classification suggested by Crocker and Henderson utilizes only four basic qualities.

The early classifications were destined to fall short of their goal because they were offered at a time when many basic data on olfactory discrimination were not available. In fact, we still lack much of the data that would be desirable before making a final assault on the question of the basic stimulus dimensions for smell.

Smell

TABLE 6-1

Classifications of Primary Odors

Linnaeus	Zwaardemaker	Henning	Crocker and Henderson
Aromatic	Ethereal	Spicy	Fragrant
Fragrant	Aromatic	Fragrant	Acid
Ambrosial	Fragrant	Putrid	Burned
Alliaceous	Ambrosial	Ethereal	Coprylic
Hircine	Alliaceous	Resinous	
Foul	Burned	Burned	
Nauseous	Coprylic		
	Repulsive		
	Nauseous		

The Nature of Olfactory Stimulation

One of the characteristics of olfactory stimuli is that they are substances that are volatile, that is, they appear in gaseous form. When an odorous material, such as a perfume, is applied in its liquid state directly to the sensitive areas of the nose, its odor is difficult to detect.

It has been estimated that we are sensitive to many thousands of vaporous materials, most of them complex organic compounds. We seem to be sensitive to very few of the simple chemical elements in the periodic table, perhaps no more than six or seven of them, most of them being in Group VII, the halogens. This group includes fluorine, chlorine, bromine, and iodine.

One large class of organic compounds to which we are sensitive is the group called the hydrocarbons. These are compounds made up of combinations of carbon and hydrogen. One of the simplest series of the hydrocarbons is the paraffin, or the methane, series. Members in this series satisfy the general constitutional formula C_nH_{2n+2}, which means that if n is the number of atoms of carbon, the number of hydrogen atoms is $2n + 2$. Methane is the simplest member of this series, having the formula CH_4.

Another hydrocarbon series is the benzene series. This group has the formula C_nH_{2n-6}, with n never less than 6. One of its members is benzene, C_6H_6. This series is particularly important to us because of the benzene ring in substances the chemist labels aromatic compounds. The label "benzene ring" comes from the usual structural diagram of such substances, a series of hexagons with six carbon atoms at the points of the hexagons. Many members of other hydrocarbons series are familiar for their distinctive odors. For example, naphthalene, $C_{10}H_8$, a white crystalline material familiar to us as moth balls, has a strong and distinctive odor.

Many of the compounds used in olfactory research have formulas that are much more complex than the ones already mentioned. We shall not go into the details of the chemical structure of olfactory stimuli because of the present uncertainty about exactly what aspects of the structure are important. Nevertheless, we should realize that it will eventually be necessary to have detailed

Smell

information about the structure of these chemicals before we will be in a position to clarify the nature of olfactory stimuli.

Absolute Threshold Measurements

Examples of numerical values of some olfactory thresholds for human beings are shown in Table 6-2. These may be expressed in many units. One dimension frequently used is the weight of the material per unit volume of air. We must be careful, of course, not to make the mistake of judging the absolute sensitivity of the olfactory system simply by looking at the magnitudes of the numbers used in stating the threshold intensities. It is obvious that such numbers can be made very large or very small simply by changing the units of weight and volume used. In Table 6-2 we use numbers of milligrams per liter of air, a very common dimension. We could also use grams per liter, which would make the numerical values one thousand times smaller. There is, at present, no rational basis for selecting one of these dimensional units over the others. It could be argued that the volume unit should be the volume typically associated with a sniff, a volume of the order of 20 to 100 cubic centimeters (cc); however, the sniff is a variable quantity and it is doubtful that anything would be gained by such a convention.

TABLE 6-2

Some Typical Thresholds for the Sense of Smell

| | Thresholds | |
Test Material	Measured in Milligrams per Liter	Measured in Number of Gram Molecules per Liter
Ethyl ether	5.8	8×10^{-5}
Ethyl mercaptan	.046	7×10^{-7}
Amyl acetate	.039	3×10^{-7}
Butyric acid	.009	1×10^{-7}
Propyl mercaptan	.006	8×10^{-8}

If we use the blast-injection technique, it is possible to specify the number of molecules of the odorous material required at threshold. This provides a dimension for stating threshold values that offers many advantages, yet any final decision on the appropriate dimension must depend in part on the nature of the psychophysical data and on our theories of sensory excitation. For materials to which we are most sensitive, such as musk or mercaptan, we require quantities of molecules in the range of millions of millions. Such large numbers suggest that we are not very sensitive to olfactory stimuli. Not all of these molecules, however, pass over the sensory surface of the olfactory apparatus. The latter is not readily accessible, as we shall see later, and the sensory structures seem to be stimulated primarily by eddy currents set up in the nasal passages when we sniff. Recent work with physical models of the nasal passages suggests that less than one-hundredth of the molecules entering the nasal cavity find their way to the sensory surfaces. What fraction of these are actually absorbed or adsorbed is not known. Attempts have been made to estimate the number of molecules required by our sensory equipment; some estimates run as low as 40 molecules, although most estimates are many times larger than this.

As we increase the exposure time, the number of molecules per second that we must present to a subject to reach his threshold gradually decreases. This result is analogous to the findings in other sense modalities. Once again we must be careful in interpreting this result. In terms of the total number of molecules of an odorous material required, we are more sensitive to short exposures of the material than to exposures of long duration. Stated differently, as we increase the duration of exposure, we decrease the rate at which we must present molecules, but we increase the total number of molecules that are required for a threshold discrimination. Examples of these two relations are shown in Figure 6-1 for mercaptan.

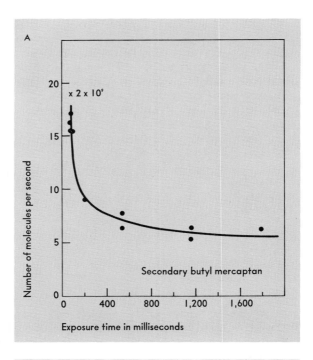

Figure 6-1. Absolute olfactory threshold as a function of the exposure duration of the stimulus. (A) Thresholds expressed in terms of number of molecules per second. (B) Thresholds expressed in terms of number of molecules. (H. deVries and M. Stuiver. In W.A. Rosenblith (ed.). Sensory communication. New York: Wiley, 1964.)

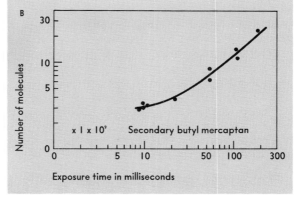

Regardless of the units used in expressing thresholds, there is no doubt that the olfactory system is a good detector. We can detect many materials in quantities measured in micrograms (a millionth of a gram). The number of molecules involved in such thresholds is large, but it compares favorably with those involving ordinary chemical testing procedures.

Adaptation and Masking

If we measure the change in threshold for the detection of an odorous substance as a function of the amount of time we have been exposed to it, we obtain results such as those shown in Figure 6-2. This figure tells us that increasing the adaptation time increases the threshold, at least over the first several minutes of adaptation. We also see that the threshold changes more rapidly when we are exposed to a high intensity of the odor than when we are exposed to a low intensity. This rate of adaptation is known to be different for different odors.

It is clear that olfactory adaptation is selective. If we adapt to one smell and then measure the threshold for a number of others, we find that the threshold for some substances is not seriously affected by adaptation, the threshold for others is affected to an intermediate degree, and the change in threshold is greatest for the adapting stimulus. Thus, each adapting stimulus leaves its own spectrum of threshold changes for all other odorous materials. An example of this type of result is shown in Figure 6-3. In each graph in this figure the solid bar represents the threshold change for the substance used as the adapting stimulus.

The combination of selective adaptation and the different rates of adaptation for different qualities leads to some important practical consequences. It means that we cannot be assured that an odorous substance, made up of a complex set of basic odor qualities, will smell the same throughout the course

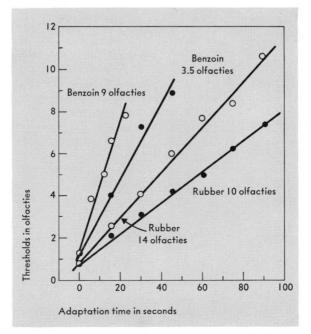

Figure 6-2. Olfactory adaptation for two concentrations of benzoin and two concentrations of rubber. Adaptation is faster for benzoin than for rubber; for each substance, adaptation is faster for the stronger concentration. (C. Pfaffmann. In S.S. Stevens (ed.). Handbook of experimental psychology. New York: Wiley, 1951.)

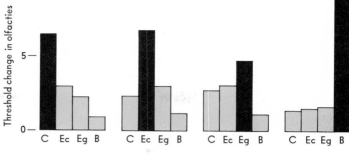

Figure 6-3. The selective character of adaptation is shown by the change in threshold following adaptation to each of four substances (C, camphor; Ec, eucalyptol; Eg, eugenol; B, benzaldehyde). The solid bars show the change in threshold for adaptation to the same stimulus, while the other bars represent the change in threshold for the remaining three stimuli. Note that the adaptation to the same stimulus alters the threshold for that stimulus much more than for other stimuli. (C. Pfaffmann. In S.S. Stevens (ed.). Handbook of experimental psychology. *New York: Wiley, 1951.)*

of a long exposure. We may adapt at different rates to different components of the stimulus and the combination of the remaining active components may differ markedly from the original mixture.

The phenomenon of masking is also observed in the study of olfaction. These masking effects are selective in the same sense as the changes observed as a result of adaptation.

Intensity Discrimination

We are able to detect the difference between two concentrations of the same volatile material, and this discrimination is analogous to the discrimination of the intensity differences already discussed in other sense modalities. Sensitivity to intensity differences does not seem to be as well developed in the sense of smell as, for example, in the sense of hearing and vision. Of course, we must be careful in comparing the senses in an absolute way because we do not now have the theoretical machinery for comparing, say, number of molecules of mercaptan with, for example, sound-pressure level. However, for each sense modality we can measure the fractional, or percentage, increment required for detecting the change in intensity, measured in whatever units seem appropriate. It is in this sense that olfaction seems to require large changes. Although a large percentage change seems to be required for obtaining a difference threshold, the laws governing this discrimination seem to be similar to those found in the other senses; large percentage changes are required when we study this discrimination at low concentrations; smaller percentage changes are required at high concentrations. The curve relating this threshold percentage change to the intensity level at which we measure the threshold seems to have the same shape as the curves found in vision and audition. The results from one such experiment on intensity discrimination are shown in Figure 6-4.

Physical Characteristics of the Stimulus

We have said that a material must be volatile in order to be an effective olfactory stimulus. By this we mean to imply only that the material must occur in gaseous form. This

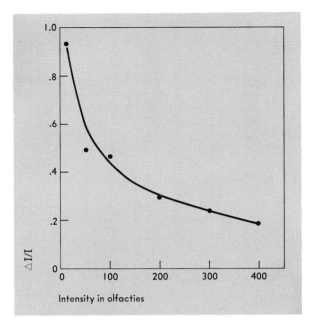

Figure 6-4. $\Delta I/I$ for india rubber. (M.J. Zigler and A.H. Holway. J gen. Psychol., *1935*, 12 372.)

does not mean that we can account for the observed differences in effectiveness of different materials simply by measuring their volatility. In fact, we know that the latter is not true. We know that different numbers of molecules are required for a threshold response to different substances. In measuring these thresholds a number of physical characteristics are involved. For example thresholds for substances in a homogenous chemical series usually vary inversely with their molecular weights, although this relationship is not a simple one. Also, the temperature of the gas influences threshold.

PHYSIOLOGICAL MECHANISMS IN OLFACTION

Structures of the Olfactory System

The sensitive region for the reception of odorous stimuli is an area of several hundred square millimeters on the upper surfaces of the nasal cavity. This area contains densely packed sense cells numbering approximately 100,000 per square millimeter. Since the surface area is several hundred square millimeters, the total number of sense cells in man is perhaps in the tens of millions. It has been estimated that the rabbit has about 100 million olfactory sense cells

The olfactory sense cells are in contact with the first-order nerves. These nerves are bipolar cells, that is, they send out two processes from the cell body. One of these processes from an olfactory sensory nerve fiber runs into the mucous lining of the nasal cavity ending in several fine cilia-like structures. The other process travels in the olfactory nerve to the olfactory bulb on the same side of the head. There it makes contact with second-order nerve cells that carry information to the higher centers of the brain.

The first major way-station for the olfactory sensory system is found in the olfactory bulb. There are three main types of cells found in the olfactory bulb: mitral cells, tufted cells, and granule cells. The connections between the olfactory nerve fibers and these second-order nerve cells are very intricate. The mitral cells, for example, send out extensions that divide profusely and intertwine with the incoming branches of the olfactory nerve fibers. The latter fibers also branch extensively when they enter the olfactory bulb, and the regions where the first- and second-order fibers meet form elaborate glomeruli. The mitral cells not only send many branches into these glomeruli, but they also send branches in the olfactory tract and carry information from the olfactory bulb to the higher centers of the brain. The tufted cells also send extensions into the glomeruli mentioned above. Therefore, they also pick up the information brought into the olfactory bulb by the olfactory nerve fibers. The tufted cells, however, send branches that extend to the glomeruli of the opposite olfactory bulb.

One point of considerable interest in interpreting the functioning of the olfactory system is the tremendous amount of convergence that must take place in the olfactory bulb. There are about 60,000 mitral cells in the olfactory bulb and the axons from these cells make up a big fraction of the fibers traveling in the olfactory nerve tract to the higher brain centers. We have already said that the number of fibers in the olfactory nerves coming into the bulb number in the tens of millions. This means that, at the level of the olfactory bulb, there is about a thousand-to-one reduction in the nerve fibers available for transmitting information to the brain. This estimate is borne out by one specific study of the anatomical connections in the rabbit, where each glomerulus receives information from 26,000 olfactory nerve fibers and passes this out through only 24 mitral cells. This thousand-to-one convergence may account, in part, for the high sensitivity we have for odorous materials.

Nerve fibers leaving the olfactory bulb form a nerve bundle called the olfactory tract. Exactly where the olfactory tract goes is not completely established. This is the only major sensory system which has no known passage to that important way-station, the thalamus. The region of the brain that represents the final projection area for the olfactory system is still poorly defined. It certainly involves the prepyriform region, but much of what was once thought to be the olfactory part of the brain is now known to be involved not with smell but with emotional behavior.

Electrical Responses in the Olfactory System

The mechanism by which odorous materials activate the sensory apparatus has not yet been clearly outlined. At various times in the history of research on olfaction it has been suggested (1) that molecules adhere to the sense cells in some way, (2) that materials radiate energy which is absorbed by the olfactory cells, (3) that the nasal cavity both radiates and absorbs radiation and that odorous materials selectively filter this radiation. Unfortunately, no one of these formulations satisfactorily encompasses enough of the experimental data.

We know that slow electrical changes occur at the surface of the olfactory epithelium, and that these electrical changes are not eliminated by concentrations of certain drugs that should eliminate nerve impulse activity in the olfactory nerves. Thus, these electrical changes are probably a measure of the activity of the sense cells. The amplitude of such electrical responses increases approximately in proportion to the logarithm of the intensity of the stimulus, which is in keeping with what we know about the action of a number of other sensory systems. The electrical response rises more rapidly, reaches a higher peak, and decays more slowly with intense stimuli than with weak stimuli. The electrical response seems to depend on the duration of the stimulus, more specifically on the waveform of the stimulus, and it also exhibits a number of adaptation effects.

The nerve fibers running from the sense-cell area to the olfactory bulb are very small, having a diameter that is only a fraction of a micron, and it has been extremely difficult to acquire information about the nature of the activity in these cells. The fibers are known to conduct impulses, but many of the exact details are not known at the present time.

The activity of nerve fibers in the olfactory bulb has also been measured, and it is clear that the amount of nerve activity increases as we increase the concentration of odorous materials. We also know that nerve activity in the bulb persists longer when we increase the duration of an odorous stimulus. It has been demonstrated that individual mitral cells are specialized in their responses. One cell will give a strong response, say, to acetone and a weak response to a substance such as eucalyptus; another mitral cell will give a weak response to acetone and a strong response to eucalyptus. There is also a regional specificity of function in the olfactory bulb. Substances that are soluble in water, such as acetone or amyl acetate, will elicit nerve activity more easily in the cells in the anterior portions of the olfactory bulb, whereas substances that are soluble in lipoids show lower thresholds in the posterior parts of the olfactory bulb. Anatomical studies have shown that the anterior portions of the bulb have mitral cells that make contact with fibers coming from the anterior and upper portions of the olfactory epithelium, while the posterior parts of the bulb contain mitral cells that come in contact with extensions of receptor cells located in the posterior and ventral portions of the olfactory epithelium.

Touch and Temperature
Sensitivity

When an object presses against the skin with sufficient intensity we say that we feel it, and this experience is different enough from the other senses to provide the basis for introducing a fifth sense into the classical list. The classes of stimuli to which the skin responds are many; things may feel rough or smooth, warm or cold, vibratory or steady. One of the questions that concerned the early workers in skin sensitivity was whether all the sensing mediated by the skin should be considered as part of a single sense modality. The question of whether we should separate the discriminations of temperature from those of touch was

87

7

answered in the affirmative at an early date. The question of whether we should consider vibratory discrimination as separate from the sense of touch was answered in the negative, although this issue was not settled until about three decades ago. With the benefit of hindsight we may not now be completely satisfied with all of the reasons that were offered in defense of these two decisions, even if we agree that the decisions were correct. However, the problem of how to define a "sense" is not easy to solve. Such problems of classification are part of the heritage from an earlier period in science, and early classifications continually return to haunt the scientist who tries to organize existing experimental data using a language that evolved before sufficient data became available.

TOUCH SENSITIVITY

Stimulus Techniques

There are a number of ways in which stimuli for the tactile system have been controlled in laboratory experiments. One of the earliest techniques for presenting stimuli of small dimensions and of adjustable pressure was to use fine hairs graded in stiffness. These are called von Frey hairs, after an early student of skin sensitivity.

Another common procedure for studying touch sensitivity, particularly adaptation phenomena, is to allow a stimulus of specified weight and size to rest freely on the skin. With this technique the displacement of the skin in the region of the stimulus is dependent on the physical characteristics of the skin. Although the physical characteristics of the skin will always enter into any consideration of the consequences of applying force or pressure, it is possible to study skin displacement systematically by using experimental procedures that force the skin to move by known amounts and at known rates. This can be done by using electromagnetic principles such as those employed in moving the loudspeaker of a radio. This, then, provides a third experimental procedure. The advantages offered by such a system derive from the fact that modern electronic techniques permit an experimenter to present calibrated amounts of force or pressure and movement to the skin and to use waveforms of almost any degree of simplicity or complexity. Step-like displacements, sinusoidal oscillations, or waveforms as complex as the pressure changes accompanying speech have been used as stimuli to the skin. It is always important to know the manner in which the skin responds to such forced movements; this will require that we understand the physical properties of the skin as a physical system. In many ways the problems we encounter here are like those involved in analyzing the auditory system.

Regional Variations in Sensitivity

Our sensitivity to tactile stimuli varies with the region of the body stimulated. We are more sensitive on hands and face than we are on the back. Some typical results showing thresholds for different regions of the body are shown in Table 7-1.

We are most familiar with pressure sensitivity involving stimuli several square millimeters in size. A more careful exploration of any of these regions of the body shows that each region is composed of smaller regions of

TABLE 7-1

Some Typical Thresholds for Touch
on Various Portions of the Skin Surface

Skin Region	Threshold in Grams per mm²
Tip of the finger	3
Forearm	8
Leg	16
Sole of the foot	250

high and low sensitivity. These small regions of high sensitivity are called touch "spots." The easiest way to demonstrate this punctate distribution of sensitivity is to draw on a subject's skin a grid of squares about one milli-meter on a side, select a stimulus of fixed intensity and present the stimulus to each square while asking the subject whether or not he feels it. These spots cannot be considered to be sharply defined regions of all-or-none sensitivity. The number of spots we find depends on the intensity of the stimulus used. In fact, there is a lawful relation between the number of touch spots obtained and the intensity of the stimulus. This relation is shown in Figure 7-1. It is clear that these spots are simply regions of higher sensitivity surrounded by regions of lower sensitivity.

This graininess in sensitivity to touch illustrates a general property of

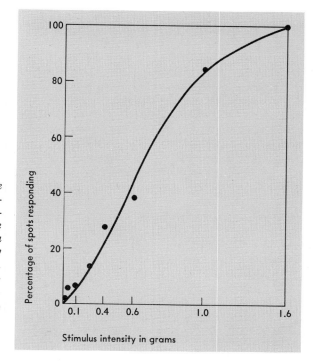

Figure 7-1. The increase in the number of pres-sure spots found respond-ing in an area of one square centimeter as a function of the intensity of the test stimulus. (Data from J.P. Guil-ford and E.M. Leuemell. J. gen. Psychol., 1936, 15, 149–159.)

skin sensitivity; we will encounter it again with temperature sensitivity where we shall find that there are also "warm" and "cold" spots on the skin. This graininess is superimposed on the gross differences in sensitivity for different regions of the body mentioned earlier.

Size of Stimulus

The sensitivity to tactile stimuli depends on many specific details of the test conditions. One of the most important of these is the size of the stimulus. As we increase the size of a stimulus we find that the force that is required to obtain a threshold response increases. That the force must be increased with increasing area suggests that perhaps the force per unit area, or the pressure, is the critical dimension determining the threshold. If we compute the threshold pressure for stimuli of different sizes, we find that threshold pressure decreases rapidly at first, then more slowly, eventually becoming a constant, as we increase the size of the test stimulus. For large areas, pressure seems to be constant at threshold. For small areas, neither force nor pressure is a constant at threshold; for these areas the relation between force and size is such that the force per linear extent of the stimulus seems to be a constant. This relation has led some investigators to suggest that the critical variable is tension, since tension is defined as force per unit length.

Adaptation

Another condition that influences touch sensitivity is the state of adaptation of the region of the skin stimulated. Several techniques have been used to study the adaptation to tactile stimuli, two of which we shall consider. The first employs a matching

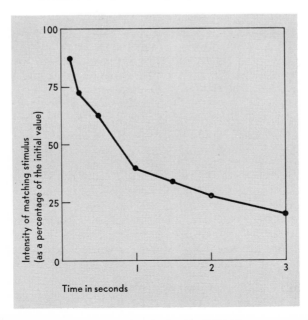

Figure 7-2. The time course of pressure adaptation. A stimulus of constant pressure was presented for four seconds to one region of the forearm. At various times during the course of this stimulus a brief comparison pressure was presented; the magnitude of this comparison stimulus was adjusted until it was judged equal to the steady pressure at that moment. These magnitudes are expressed as a percentage of the stimulus required at the onset of the steady pressure. (M.J. Zigler. Am. J. Psych., 1932, 44, 709.)

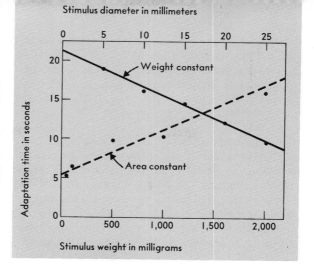

Figure 7-3. Adaptation times to pressure stimulus when the area of the stimulus is held constant and the weight varied (broken line), and when the weight is held constant and the area varied (solid line). (R.S. Woodworth and H. Schlosberg. Experimental psychology (Revised ed.). New York: Holt, Rinehart and Winston, 1955.)

procedure. We present a stimulus to one region of a subject's skin, and, at various times after the onset of that adapting stimulus, we present a brief comparison stimulus to another region, adjusting its magnitude until the subject says that it matches the adapting stimulus in intensity. If we express the magnitude of the chosen comparison stimulus as a fraction of the value needed to achieve a match at the onset of the adapting stimulus, we obtain the curve shown in Figure 7-2. This curve shows us that adaptation to steady tactile stimuli is very rapid; the magnitude of the comparison stimulus shows substantial changes in a matter of seconds.

Another technique that has been used for studying pressure adaptation is to measure the time to complete adaptation. If we study adaptation using weights resting freely on the skin, we find that, over a large range of weights, a subject will eventually report that he no longer feels the stimulus. Let us call the interval from the onset of the stimulus to the time when the subject reports that he no longer detects it the adaptation time. This period will depend on the weight applied to the skin and the size of the surface in contact with the skin. Figure 7-3 shows the way in which adaptation time varies with the weight of the stimulus; the two curves represent the results using two different stimulus areas. The heavier the weight, the longer the adaptation time; the larger the stimulus area, the shorter the adaptation time.

In using weights resting freely on the surface of the skin, we must be concerned with the question of how the skin responds to the stimulus. Obviously, the skin will be deformed; yet we know that it will not be stretched indefinitely. It will offer some resistance to the fall of the weight in such a way that the weight falls rapidly at first and then more slowly.

Our adaptation to such stimuli suggests that pressure at the surface of the skin cannot be the critical variable because pressure has been constant throughout the exposure period. This is true because pressure, as a physical variable, is defined as the force per unit area. Since the rate of displacement changes during the exposure period, the suggestion has been made that the important consideration is the movement of the skin produced by tactile stimuli. This argument maintains that the report of complete adaptation

Touch and
Temperature
Sensitivity

91

occurs when the movement of the skin reaches some critical value. This notion seems plausible; the application of any force or pressure on the skin is going to lead to some adjustment of the skin, and this displacement (or some function of it, such as velocity) could serve as the adequate stimulus for activating the tactile system. Yet this view encounters some difficulties for the rate at which the stimuli are moving at the time of adaptation is not a constant for different sizes and weights of stimuli. In other words, the rate of movement at the surface of the skin is not an invariant. It is possible to escape this difficulty by assuming that the critical variable is the movement of some portion of tissue not directly at the site of contact between the stimulus and the surface of the skin. This notion is not easy to test experimentally because we do not know exactly what portion of the skin to monitor. It leads us to wonder whether the notion that tactile receptors are responding to the dimension of pressure may also be modified to state that the pressure we must specify is the pressure at some point other than at the surface of the skin. We could then account for adaptation by assuming that some adjustment of pressure takes place in the skin when a weight is applied.

The discussion in the preceding paragraph arises from a simple failure, a failure to find that force or pressure or some other obvious physical dimension is an ideal dimension for handling the psychophysical data. Each of these physical dimensions is precise and quantitative and each provides an exact way in which to describe tactile stimuli. However, no one of them seems to provide us with the kind of definition that describes the stimulus in terms that are directly relevant to how the system is activated. What is really required is more detailed analysis before we can be satisfied with either formulation. Both formulations require that we have an understanding of the velocity and pressure waves set up by any stimulus. This problem is simply another version of our persistent search for an adequate definition of the stimulus.

Two-point Threshold

One of the classical measures of tactile acuity is the two-point threshold. This is analogous to the measurement of resolving power in the visual system and involves the measurement of the minimum separation of two tactile stimuli that can just be detected as "two." Tactile acuity is known to vary from one region of the body to the other and some representative thresholds are shown in Table 7-2, along with measurements of the error of localization. These results also

TABLE 7-2

Tactile Acuity Measured by the Two-point Threshold
and the Error of Localization

Region *of the Skin Tested*	*Two-point Threshold* *(TPT)*	*Localization Error* *(LE)*	*Ratio* *TPT/LE*
Leg	67.5	15.7	4.3
Forearm	40.5	8.5	4.3
Forehead	22.5	6.3	3.6
Lips	4.5	1.1	4.1

Touch and
Temperature
Sensitivity

give an indication of spatial resolution; they are obtained in the following way. A person is blindfolded and the experimenter touches some point on the skin, marking it at the same time; the subject is asked to touch the same spot. The distance separating these two points is measured as the error of localization. One interesting characteristic of the data shown in the table is the stability of the ratio of these two measures of spatial resolution, the two-point threshold and the localization error.

Vibratory Sensitivity

The tactile sensory system has the capacity to respond to repetitive pressure stimuli. Experimentally, the study of vibratory sensitivity in the skin is similar in many ways to the study of audibility. For example, we can measure the magnitude of alternating pressure required for detection, using sinusoidal stimuli of different frequencies. Such an experiment yields data that are, in general form, similar to those obtained when we study audibility thresholds (see, for example, Figure 3-5). Some examples of the data obtained on the tactile system are shown in Figure 7-4. Although similarities exist, the differences between the vibratory-sensitivity curve and the audibility curve are perhaps more important than the similarities. Two striking differences show up when we look carefully at the numbers associated with the graphs. The first difference is in the region of maximum sensitivity. For touch we obtain maximum sensitivity at a frequency approximately one-tenth of that for the auditory system. The second difference has to do with the numerical values of the absolute thresholds. Although the displacements at threshold for the vibratory system are small, of the order of one micron, it is clear that they are many orders of magnitude larger than the threshold displacements of the ear drum. The minimum threshold displacements in the two cases differ by a factor of about 100,000.

We have had occasion to refer to the importance of the mechanical properties of the skin in discussing the adaptation to stimuli falling freely into the skin. These mechanical properties are also involved in determining the response of the skin to vibratory stimulation. Bekesy has shown that vibration applied to one part of the skin surface spreads extensively over the body surface. A tactile stimulus applied to one region of the body sets up a traveling wave that may spread many inches and, if intense enough, may spread the full length of the body. The attempt to discover the manner in which we are

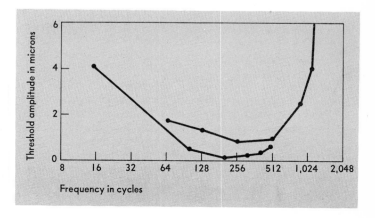

Figure 7-4. Vibration thresholds for different frequencies of vibration measured on the finger tip. (Modified from F.A. Geldard. Fundamentals of psychology. New York: Wiley, 1962.)

able to localize the source of these vibrations when the vibrations are so wide-spread raises questions very similar to the questions raised in discussing auditory mechanisms. We have suggested that part of this sharpening in the auditory system is neural in nature. Less is known about how sharpening is achieved in the tactile system, but Bekesy has shown that if one applies to the skin a large-scale duplicate of the vibration patterns observed in the ear (so that, for example, most of the forearm is set into vibration), a subject will report that he feels the vibration sharply localized in one small region.

TEMPERATURE SENSITIVITY

The physical dimension used in the study of discriminations of temperature and temperature differences is familiar to all of us. The Fahrenheit scale is in everyday use by all of us; the centigrade scale is perhaps the most frequently used scale in laboratory work in the sciences; the absolute temperature scale is encountered less frequently, but is of great importance in physical theory. These scales represent quantitative statements about the concept of temperature. They differ in their zero point and in the size of the degree unit, but there are exact rules for transforming one scale into the others.

Discriminations of warmth and coolness are obtained from the manipulation of this single physical dimension. The psychophysics of temperature sensitivity encounters its first difficulty with the discovery that a given temperature may yield a response of "warm," "cold," or "neutral" depending on the state of a subject's sensory system at the time the stimulus is presented. We can illustrate this by doing a simple experiment. If a subject immerses his two hands in separate containers filled with water at skin temperature, say 32° centigrade, he will report that the water is neither warm nor cold. If we now have the subject place his right hand in a container of water at 29°C he will say that it feels cool; if he places the left hand in a container of water at 35°C he will report that it feels warm. If the subject keeps his left and right hands in these second containers for several minutes and then places them back in the containers filled with water at 32°C, he will report that his right hand is in warm water and his left hand is in cold water. Thus, 32°C may be reported as neutral, warm, or cold depending on the test conditions. What we call warm and cold, then, depends on the adaptation temperature.

We achieved these results by using the phenomenon of temperature adaptation. Such adaptation effects are prominent in the study of temperature sensitivity, and, because they can cause a shift in our response from warm to cold and vice versa, they have led to the concept of a "physiological zero."

Adaptation

Temperature adaptation may be studied quantitatively in a variety of ways. One technique that has been used to study the time course of adaptation is to have a subject make judgments of equality of temperature for stimuli presented to two different regions of the skin. With this technique both regions are first adapted to the same temperature. One region is then presented with a new adapting temperature, while the other region is maintained at the initial temperature. For example, we might initially adapt both hands for five or ten minutes to a

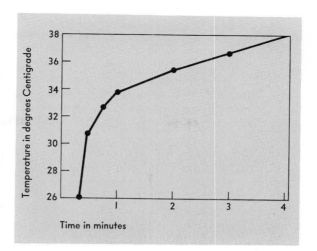

Figure 7-5. The time course of temperature adaptation (see text). (R.S. Woodworth and H. Schlosberg. Experimental psychology (Revised ed.). New York: Holt, Rinehart and Winston, 1955.)

temperature of 38°C. At the end of this preliminary exposure, we immerse the left hand in water having a temperature of 26°C. At regular intervals of time following the onset of this new adaptation stimulus, we present test stimuli of varying temperature to the right hand (which is being maintained at 38°C) and ask the subject to report whether the test temperatures are warmer, equal to, or colder than the temperature to which the left hand is being adapted. Experimental results from such an experiment are shown in Figure 7-5. This illustration shows us that the right hand initially requires a stimulus temperature of 26° to achieve an equality match with the adapting stimulus of 26°C applied to the left hand. This is what we might expect. After 30 seconds, a temperature of 31° presented to the right hand is judged as equal to 26° exposed to the adapted hand. Gradually the matching temperature rises to 38°, reaching this point after approximately four minutes of adaptation. In other words, the temperature of 38°C for one hand seems to establish a "physiological" zero point that is equivalent to the "physiological" zero established by the 26° stimulus in the other hand. These results seem to hold for a range of temperatures extending approximately 10° above and below skin temperature. There is, though, some disagreement in the experimental literature about the exact range of temperatures over which one can obtain complete temperature adaptation. Some authors feel that this range may be considerably smaller than the amount just stated.

The time required for a subject to adapt completely to temperatures near skin temperature depends on how far away the adaptation temperature is from the normal skin temperature. If we measure the adaptation times required to have the subject report that the stimuli are no longer warm or cold, we obtain the results shown in Figure 7-6. It is clear from this figure that the farther away from skin temperature the adapting temperature is, the longer it will take to adapt completely to the temperature.

Around any temperature to which we completely adapt there is a region that constitutes a neutral zone. The size of this neutral zone increases as we adapt to temperatures away from the normal skin temperature. If we work with a subject having a skin temperature of 32°C, we find that he is able to

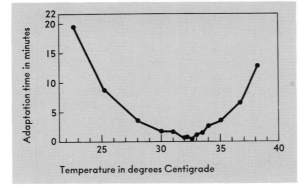

Figure 7-6. Time required to adapt to temperature stimulation as a function of stimulus temperature. (H. Hensel. Arch. ges. Physiol., 1950, 252, 165.)

report reliably that a temperature about one-tenth of a degree higher feels warm; with equal reliability he will judge that a temperature about one-tenth of a degree below skin temperature feels cool. Thus, near skin temperature the thresholds for warmth and cold are approximately 0.1°C. If we adapt the subject to temperatures other than skin temperature, these thresholds become larger.

Since the size of the neutral zone varies with adaptation temperature, we might suspect that the process of changing the physiological zero point is not a simple sliding of the temperature scale. Support for this suspicion comes from another experiment. Suppose we expose one region of the skin to 15°C and another area to 30°C and, after several minutes, test for the pairs of

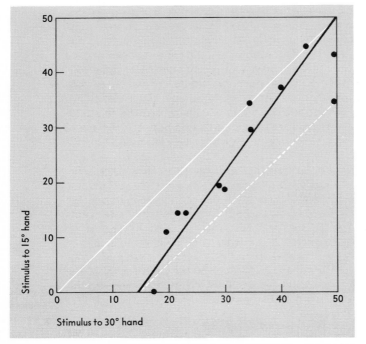

Figure 7-7. Stimulus temperatures judged as equal when the two hands have been adapted to different temperatures (see text). (Data from E. Hummel. Arch. ges. Psychol., 1926, 57, 305–394.)

temperatures (presented to these two regions) that will be judged as equal. We can see the results of such an experiment in Figure 7-7. If adaptation had no effect on either region, we would expect that the temperatures that would be judged as being equal would, on the average, be physically equal. Such an outcome is shown schematically by the solid white line in Figure 7-7. If the effect of the differential adaptation of the two regions was simply to slide the temperature scale of each region so that they had zero points 15° apart, we would expect the results represented by the dashed line in Figure 7-7. The experimental points in this figure clearly show that neither of these outcomes is observed. Although there is some variability in the equality settings, the black line representing the data suggests that there is (1) a shift in the zero point, and (2) a shift in the size of the scale units. This result is analogous to the differences that exist between the Fahrenheit and the Centigrade scales. By this differential adaptation we have lowered the zero point for one region so that it is 15° below that for the other region. We have also changed the size of the scale units by approximately 40 per cent. This is like the change we introduce when we translate the Fahrenheit scale to the Centigrade scale; in the latter case we change the zero point by 32° and the scale units by the fraction nine-fifths.

The Effect of Size and Location of the Stimulus

The experiments discussed so far involved the stimulation of large areas of the skin. The typical technique has been to immerse a subject's hand in a container of water whose temperature is accurately controlled. There are a number of other experimental techniques for measuring temperature sensitivity. One method in common use employs small hollow metal stimulators whose temperature is controlled by water flowing through them. This technique allows us to stimulate extremely small areas of the skin. All such stimuli involve tactile, as well as temperature, stimulation. There are some techniques, however, that attempt to avoid the involvement of the tactile system; one of these utilizes infrared radiation. The infrared region of the electromagnetic spectrum can be focused in the same manner as we focus visible light, and precise control over the duration and the size of the stimulus can be achieved by techniques quite analogous to those employed in the study of vision. Such techniques are available when we wish to study the nature of responses to warm stimuli. Some difficulties are encountered when we attempt to employ comparable procedures in studying sensitivity to cold. One approximate procedure places near the surface of the skin a small metal stimulator whose temperature is maintained by cold water or dry ice.

Any technique that permits us to present very small stimuli of adjustable temperature to the skin reveals that our temperature sensitivity has a punctate distribution similar to that found in the study of the tactile system. Exploring the surface of the skin with warm or cold stimuli shows that there are points of high sensitivity—warm spots and cold spots—surrounded by regions of relatively low sensitivity. All regions of the body with both warm and cold sensitivity have more cold spots than warm spots, usually in a ratio of about eight or ten to one. A few regions of the body, such as the central part of the cornea of the eye, seem to possess no temperature sensitivity; they will respond to touch and to pain, but not to temperature.

As in the case of the sensitivity to tactile stimuli, the fine-grain sensitivity differences shown by the warm and cold spots are overlaid on gross differences in temperature sensitivity from one region of the body to another. Table 7-3 shows some typical measurements of the number of warm and cold spots in different parts of the body.

TABLE 7-3

Distribution of Warm and Cold Spots in Human Skin [a]

Parts of Body	Cold Spots [b]	Warm Spots [c]
Forehead	5.5–8	
Nose	8–13	1
Lips	16–19	
Other parts of face	8.5–9	1.7
Chest	9–10.2	0.3
Abdomen	8–12.5	
Back	7.8	
Upper arm	5–6.5	
Forearm	6–7.5	0.3–0.4
Back of hand	7.4	0.5
Palm of hand	1–5	0.4
Finger dorsal	7–9	1.7
Finger volar	2–4	1.6
Thigh	4.5–5.2	0.4
Calf	4.3–5.7	
Back of foot	5.6	
Sole of foot	3.4	

[a] Number per cm^2.
[b] After Strughold and Porz.
[c] After Rein.

"Paradoxical" Temperature Discriminations

One of the classical problems in the study of temperature sensitivity comes from what is called "paradoxical cold." Stimulus temperatures in a range that subjects usually report as warm will, if applied to a cold spot, frequently lead to a report of cold. You may have experienced this phenomenon with the first drops from a warm shower, which frequently seems cold. This is not the same problem raised at the beginning of the chapter when we pointed out that particular temperatures could be labeled as neutral, warm, or cold depending on the state of adaptation. Specialized adaptation is not involved in this case. In this instance, a region is stimulated that will lead to reports of cold if stimuli below skin temperature are used, it will typically not lead to reports of warm if temperatures above skin temperature are used. If the temperatures are in an appropriate range (around 45°C), they are reported as cold.

There are experiments indicating that an analogous phenomenon, called "paradoxical warm," can be found using stimuli that would ordinarily be labeled cold. This seems to be a less predictable event, and we encounter it less frequently in everyday life. There is one experimental finding that may account for the difficulty of obtaining reliable reports of "paradoxical warm," if such a phenomenon exists. The problem may arise from the difference in the reaction time of these two temperature senses. Measurements of our ability to react to temperature stimuli clearly show that the reaction time to warmth is longer than that to cold. This fact has been used in the past to argue that the sense cells for cold sensitivity are located nearer to the surface of the skin than are the sense cells for warmth. We shall discuss this problem later when we review some of the evidence concerning temperature mechanisms. In the present context it suggests that (1) if a temperature above the one to which the skin is adapted is presented, and (2) if it stimulates both the warm receptors and some of the cold receptors that respond in the paradoxical cold region, the action of these cold receptors would precede the action of the warm receptors; this could lead to a report of cold. In the opposite condition, however, where we are presenting a stimulus below the adaptation temperature and where we might be stimulating warm receptors in a "paradoxical" manner along with cold receptors, it may be that the cold receptors mask out the feeling of paradoxical warmth because of the shorter latency of the cold receptors.

PHYSIOLOGICAL MECHANISMS FOR TOUCH AND TEMPERATURE SENSITIVITY

The punctate distribution of sensitivity in touch and temperature suggests that there may be specialized receptors in the skin linked specifically to these sensitivities. The early histological studies of the skin demonstrated that (1) some of the sensory nerve fibers in the skin ended as profusely branching free nerve terminals and that (2) some of the sensory fibers ended in one or more of a variety of special encapsulating structures. Since there are variations in the relative density of both free nerve endings and encapsulated structures, and since there are regional variations in tactile and temperature sensitivity, many attempts were made to establish some correlation between histological structure and sensory experience. In fact, a number of heroic experiments were performed by early research workers in skin sensitivity. For example, these experimenters would map the touch and/or warm or cold spots for a small part of their skin, stain these spots, then excise the skin, section it, and examine it under a microscope to see whether the stained regions corresponded to the location of any particular type of sensory ending.

In spite of the heroism involved, the most that can be said about this question of the link between a particular sense modality and a type of encapsulated ending is that it is still being debated. The evidence for specialized functioning is very limited. Some early views of the problem have been widely propagated in secondary sources, such as textbooks in physiology and psychology, but the evidence for these views is far from firm. A common textbook statement is that touch is probably mediated by a number of endings: structures called Meissner corpuscles, Merkel discs, and the complex of free nerve endings at the base of hair follicles. Warmth is assumed to be mediated by structures called Ruffini endings, cold by Krause end-bulbs. These linkages are based on varying amounts of information; little of it is very convincing.

There is substantial evidence on one type of sense cell found in the deeper layers of the skin and distributed generously throughout the body (in the mesentery, in subcutaneous tissue, and in the tissue around muscle). This cell is called the Pacinian corpuscle. It forms an onion-like encapsulation on a nerve ending; it is a spherical structure, with many layers, all laminated around a central core that houses the ending of a peripheral nerve. Pressure applied to this cell will deform the cell and set up a local potential change that serves to initiate nerve impulses in the sensory fiber. It is clear that this sense cell is pressure-sensitive and that it can respond to pressure changes and to vibratory stimuli. We have no comparable information on any of the other types of specialized endings that have been offered as mediating mechanisms for skin sensitivity. We can only leave unanswered questions about the specific sensory apparatus that serves the touch and temperature senses.

When we turn to the results that have been obtained from electrical recordings of the messages in sensory nerves, we find that the picture becomes much clearer. It is possible to record from individual nerve fibers that are primarily responsive to tactile stimulation, from others that are primarily responsive to decreases in temperature, and from others that are primarily responsive to increases in temperature. If we record from nerve fibers responsive to pressure stimulation we find that pressure applied to the skin yields a brief burst of impulses; the number of impulses obtained and the rate at which the impulses occur will depend on the magnitude of the pressure. If a steady pressure is maintained, the impulses will quickly cease; physiologically, the tactile system adapts rapidly and completely to steady pressure. If a vibrating stimulus is presented, the nerve fiber will fire repetitively, in bursts that are paced by the repetition rate of the stimulus. The nerve will follow this repetition easily if the rate of pressure alternation is slow; at higher rates of alternation the responses to the separate stimulus pulses will not longer clearly signal the repetition rate of the stimulus.

The nerve fibers sensitive to tactile stimuli tend to be fibers of large diameter, therefore the impulses tend to be larger and tend to travel faster than those serving temperature sensitivity. However, this is only an approximate rule because there are fibers of small diameter that are known to respond to either touch or temperature.

For the temperature sense we find both "warm" and "cold" fibers. The labels "warm" and "cold" fibers refer to systems separated on the basis of two specific properties. First, "cold" fibers are nerve cells that will increase their rate of firing if temperature is decreased; "warm" fibers are cells that increase their rate of firing if the temperature is increased. The second distinction between these fibers is in the range of temperatures to which they respond. When a change in temperature is introduced the fiber will first exhibit a transient change in the rate of impulse discharge and then settle down to a steady rate of discharge. If we look at this "resting" rate of firing as a function of the stimulus temperature, we see that we obtain different functions for "warm" and "cold" fibers. An example of the results is shown in Figure 7-8.

As an experimental variable, temperature offers a number of pitfalls for the person interested in sensory systems. The normal functioning of a nerve cell depends on the action of a complex biochemical system which we know is affected by temperature. In fact, it seems to be possible to initiate activity in any peripheral nerve fiber by altering its temperature in an appropriate way. Nerve tissue is, in some ways, directly suited to serve as a temperature detector. However, the work on warm and cold fibers seems to offer us con-

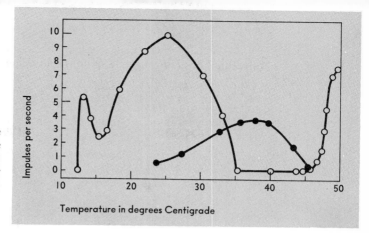

Figure 7-8. The impulse frequency of a single cold fiber (open circles) and a single warm fiber (solid circles) as a function of temperature. (Y. Zotterman. Ann. Rev. Physiol., 1953, 15, 357.)

siderably more in the way of a mechanism for temperature sensitivity than would be found in a typical study of the effect of temperature on normal nerve conduction. Although many fibers respond to temperature changes, the amount of temperature change required is too large to make the results convincing as a possible mechanism for the psychophysical data with which we wish to deal. More specifically, what is required is some change in, or addition to, this general property of peripheral nerve activity so as to bring the observations into approximate numerical agreement with the psychophysical data. We seem to have this change in the case of the "warm" and "cold" fibers. For example, the most sensitive of the warm and cold fibers will respond to temperature changes of the order of 0.1°C. This sensitivity corresponds closely to the psychophysical threshold data.

This point illustrates another feature of any search for physiological mechanisms that may mediate the behavioral data. At an early stage of exploration of any sensory system, analogies and gross approximations may serve a useful purpose in guiding our thinking about how the sensory system works. Our eventual goal, however, must be to establish a correspondence between the physiological data and the behavioral data, a correspondence that must be more than generally reasonable, it must be numerically sensible. We saw an example of this problem in studying the visual system. There we encountered substantial evidence that a photochemical cycle was involved in initiating activity in the visual system. However, we also found it necessary to abandon one plausible explanation for the data of light- and dark-adaptation, namely that sensitivity changes in adaptation are due directly to the changes in the concentration of the absorbing material. Although the notion was initially reasonable, it did not hold up in the light of additional experimental analysis, for the numerical changes in concentration did not agree with the changes required by this particular view of adaptation.

In addition to the numerical agreement between the threshold for warm and cold fibers and the behavioral threshold, there is one feature of the data in Figure 7-8 that bears on this discussion of an appropriate mechanism for temperature discrimination. We refer to the shape of the curve showing the response of the cold fiber. This curve exhibits high responsiveness above about 45°C. From a strictly physiological point of view this result is somewhat unexpected. The importance of this result rests in its correlation with

Touch and Temperature Sensitivity

an equally surprising psychophysical result already discussed, the phenomenon of "paradoxical" cold. Both the psychophysical phenomemon and the physiological phenomenon occur in the same region of the temperature scale. This graph simply tells us that some nerve fibers equipped to signal the presence of low temperatures and decreases in temperature, and therefore called cold fibers, exhibit a responsiveness to a restricted range of higher temperatures. Interestingly enough, this range corresponds to that eliciting paradoxical-cold responses in human subjects.

As we move from the peripheral to the central nervous system we find the specificity of the tactile and temperature sense, exhibited in the peripheral sensory fiber, maintained. In the spinal cord, fibers group according to function, temperature separate from touch, and travel in different bundles. These temperature and touch fibers project to overlapping areas in the thalamus and in the cortex, but the separation of the senses is retained in that individual fibers can be found that will respond differently to touch and temperature. There are, of course, fibers that will respond to both types of stimulation, but this modality mixing is not limited to touch and temperature.

The representation in the brain of the sensitivity of skin surfaces shows an interesting kind of distortion. This representation involves considerable stretching and area distortion. The relative amounts of the brain devoted to to the various regions of the body correspond roughly to the resolving power of the tactile system. Regions of the body that have good spatial resolution—that is, small two-point thresholds—have large areas of the brain devoted to them. Thus, the brain area serving touch sensitivity of the lips and fingers is relatively much larger than that devoted to the skin of the back. Figure 7-9 shows the body as it appears if we draw the size of the different parts of the body proportional to the amount of brain tissue devoted to them.

Figure 7-9. Diagram of sections cut through sensory and motor cortices, representing body parts as measured by evoked potentials. (Redrawn from W. Penfield and T. Rasmussen, The cerebral cortex of man. New York: Macmillan, 1952.)

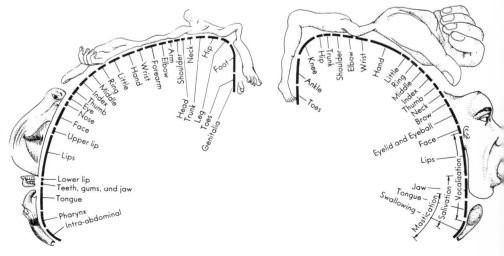

SENSORY   MOTOR

Vestibular
and Kinesthetic Senses

One of the most difficult tasks in sensory psychology is to deal with the kinesthetic and vestibular senses. The psychophysical data in these areas is substantially more limited than in senses already discussed. This lack is no reflection of the relative importance of these systems; on the contrary, these systems provide us with information necessary for maintaining most of the subtle features of our normal, coordinated behavior patterns. The situation was appropriately described in 1914 by J. B. Watson, the founder of modern behaviorism, in his book *Behavior*. He said, "If we made the statement that all of the work upon habit formation

103

8

in all of the behavior laboratories . . . points to the fact that the kinesthetic sense is the most important system of receptors, and yet that there was not one single thing that we could say about this sense in isolation, paradoxical as it might seem, it would not be far from the truth." Fortunately, the situation today is not that devastating, yet recently one of the leading textbooks in experimental psychology mentioned kinesthesis in only one sentence, and this sentence simply stated that one of the first senses to be separated from the sense of touch was kinesthesis.

Because much of the early history of sensory psychology centered on the study of conscious sensory experience, it is understandable that the kinesthetic and vestibular senses came in for secondary consideration. These systems are largely "silent" systems—we do not have a rich vocabulary for describing what we "sense" with them. We are likely to appreciate their importance only when they are absent. We tend not to be impressed with our ability to stand erect and walk in a coordinated fashion in the dark or when we are blindfolded; nor are we impressed with the subtleties of the quick body adjustments we can make when we begin to slip or fall, or when someone bumps against us. We may be impressed in a negative way with the vestibular sense, if we are prone to sea or air sickness. When so afflicted we may wonder why we need such a system; we may not be aware of the difficulties we would encounter if we lacked the normal information provided by this sense.

VESTIBULAR SYSTEM

Over 130 years ago Flourens described some of the consequences of damage to the semicircular canals, the sensory apparatus of the vestibular system, and no more convincing demonstration of the importance of vestibular information is required. He showed, for example, that damage to just one of the three canals on one side of the head in birds inhibits all voluntary flight. If a bird is forced into the air, his flight is crude and he quickly descends. Removal of all three canals on one side of the head interferes with the ability of the bird to maintain a standing position; he repeatedly somersaults and will attempt to maintain appropriate posture to the point of exhaustion.

Damage to these structures in man also demonstrates the importance of the information they supply. Damage to the semicircular canals on just one side produces extreme dizziness, nausea, and vomiting; there are also changes in heart beat, blood pressure, and perspiration. Typically, the affected individual is unable to maintain normal erect posture.

The description of these symptoms immediately suggests one of the problems in studying this sensory system. Most of the reactions we have described are what we ordinarily label as reflex in nature. They involve the autonomic nervous system, such as changes in heart beat and blood pressure, or the mechanisms of coordination of bodily movements.

Although we encounter difficulties, it is possible to obtain psychophysical data on the vestibular system. The semicircular canals respond to movements of the body in space; therefore, the first data we shall look at are measurements of the thresholds for detecting motion. The most generally accepted view is that the semicircular canals respond to acceleration, rather than to the speed of movement. The prevalence of this view is based partly on early theoretical analyses of the action of the semicircular canals, and partly on the fact that we quickly adapt to steady rates of movement. After a short exposure to a constant speed, we cannot discriminate how fast we are moving, or even that we are moving, unless we are provided with cues through some other sensory system, for example, through the eyes. If we blindfold a subject and begin to rotate him, increasing the speed of rotation from zero to some fixed value, he will report that he is in motion while the speed is increasing. Shortly after the speed stabilizes, he will not be able to detect that he is in motion. If, after the subject has been rotating at constant speed, we decrease the speed to zero, the subject again will be able to detect motion during the period of change. These periods of increasing and decreasing speeds of rotation are periods of acceleration and deceleration.

In the discussion that follows we shall refer to data obtained from experiments employing rotary motion. In these cases we usually express the movement in angular units. For example, we speak of angular speed in units such as degrees per second; we speak of angular acceleration as the rate of change of speed, as in degrees per second per second, which will be abbreviated $°/sec^2$.

We can determine thresholds for motion in the classical way by asking a subject whether he detects motion. If we measure the threshold for reporting motion, we find that a subject can reliably report angular accelerations of less than $.5°/sec^2$. This threshold depends on the length of time during which we are exposed to acceleration. The longer the exposure time, the lower the accleration threshold. We seem to be about equally sensitive to acceleration and deceleration.

We have already emphasized that there are many reflex responses to acceleration, and one of the most sensitive of these reflex systems is the reflex movement of the eyes in response to rotation. One of the common measurements of these eye movements is what is called postrotational nystagmus. If a subject is rotated at a uniform rate and then the rotation is stopped, his eyes will move in the direction opposite to the direction of rotation. The movement of the eyes in response to rotation is, in fact, a complex sequence of responses. With the onset of rotation a slow drift of the eye in the direction of the rotation is interlaced with rapid return movements. This combination of drift in one direction and saccadic movements in the opposite direction continues during the period of acceleration, and the magnitude and frequency of these eye movements depend on the magnitude of the acceleration. Shortly after the motion stabilizes, the eyes drift in the opposite direction.

If we look at the thresholds obtained using either the verbal report or one of the variety of reflex movements, we find that the thresholds for detecting motion range from about $.1°/sec^2$ to about $.8°/sec^2$. In general, accelerations of .1 to .2 of a degree/sec^2 will yield reflex eye movements, accelerations of less than $.5°/sec^2$ will lead the subject to report motion, and accelerations of $.8°/sec^2$ will yield head movements. In all of these cases the threshold acceleration depends on the duration of exposure to it—the longer the exposure time, the lower the threshold acceleration. Over a substantial range of durations, the product of these two variables, that is, the product of threshold acceleration and duration of exposure, is a constant. This finding is reminiscent of the Bunsen-Roscoe law in vision. It suggests that for short exposures to movement the critical variable is the rate of movement and that for long exposures the critical variable is acceleration.

The sensory apparatus for the vestibular sense is found in a region intimately tied to part of the auditory system, the inner ear on each side of the head. The gross features are shown in Figure 8-1A. Three tube-like structures, called the semicircular canals, are arranged approximately at right angles to one another. One of these canals is oriented in the horizontal plane, one in the vertical plane, the third lies in the sagital plane. These planes are shown in relation to the position of the head in Figure 8-1B. The position of these canals with respect to the surface of the earth will obviously be determined by the position of the head; Figure 8-1B shows that the horizontal plane is not quite horizontal if the head is held erect.

Careful inspection of the semicircular canals shows that each canal extends out from and returns to a central structure, which we shall look at in a moment. First let us look in more detail at the canals. They are filled with a fluid and, at the base of each of these canals, there is a bulb-like enlargement, called the ampulla; it is in this region that the sensory equipment for the canals is located. A cross-section of one of these bulbous enlargements is shown in Figure 8-2. This diagram shows a basal structure, called the crista, with ciliated structures extending into a gelatinous material called the cupula. The present view is that these ciliated structures serve as the sensory apparatus and that they are stimulated by movements of the gelatinous material caused by rotation. The movements of the gelatinous material have been measured directly in fish by injecting a small amount of a dye (or a small oil droplet) into the fluid and observing the change in its position

Figure 8-1. Position of the semicircular canals in the head.

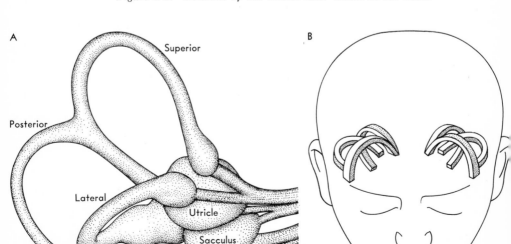

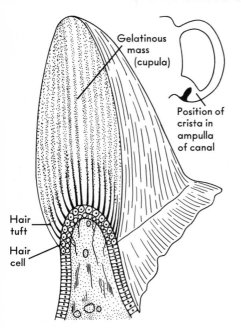

Figure 8-2. Cross section of the crista showing the gelatinous mass, hair tuft and hair cell. The small drawing shows the position of the crista in the ampulla of the semicircular canal. (E.G. Boring, et al. Introduction to psychology. New York: Wiley, 1939.)

when the system is rotated. These observations reveal that the movements of the structure within the ampulla are like those of a hinged door, which assumes different positions depending on the magnitude of the rotation. An example of these movements is shown in Figure 8-3. These displacements are induced by angular accelerations. The cupula will stay displaced with constant acceleration, if the rotation is maintained at a constant speed; that is, at zero acceleration the cupula will return to its original position within about 30 seconds.

Because of the physical orientation of the three canals, the movements within any of the three ampullae will depend on the plane in which the rotation occurs. Each would be maximally stimulated if the plane of rotation corresponded to its plane of orientation. Any particular plane of rotation would set up a particular pattern of excitation in these structures.

It was mentioned earlier that the semicircular canals are extensions from a central area; this area contains two regions of interest to us, the utricle and the saccule. These regions are also filled with fluid, the semicircular canals being continuous with the utricle. Both the utricle and the saccule contain

Figure 8-3. The effect of angular acceleration on the position of the cupula: (A) When the head is at rest. (B) When the head is accelerating. (G. Dohlman. Proc. roy. Soc. Med., 1935, 28, 1371–1380.)

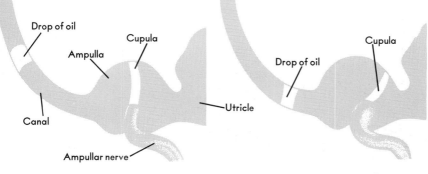

basal structures, analagous to the crista, called maculae; they contain cells with hair-like extensions that extend into the gelatinous material.

Little is known of the functioning of the saccule. There is, in fact, some doubt about its involvement in the sense of balance and orientation. Some investigators suggest that it has a residual auditory function. In lower animals, in fact, the systems we distinguish as the auditory and vestibular systems are not so easily separated.

The utricle seems to be designed to serve as a kind of gravity detector. The fluid in the utricle contains a number of particles, formed of a calcium compound, called otiliths. These particles are heavier than the material in which they are immersed and rest on the hair-like endings. Their position on the macula will be determined by the orientation of the head with respect to the direction of the gravitational pull.

Nerve cells extend from the ciliated sensory apparatus in the structures of the vestibular system to the vestibular nuclei in the medulla. These nerves make up the vestibular branch of the VIIIth cranial nerve. We have already seen that the nerve fibers from the inner ear also form part of this cranial nerve; they constitute the auditory branch. Approximately half of the fibers of the VIIIth cranial nerve serve the vestibular system, the other half serve the auditory system.

When the head is at rest, the nerve fibers from the semicircular canals seem to send a steady stream of impulses to the central nervous system. If we record nerve activity as the head is rotated, we find that the rate of discharge of impulses of a fiber from one semicircular canal will increase if the head is rotated in one direction and decrease if the head is rotated in the opposite direction. If we plot the rate of discharge in a single nerve cell during such an experiment, we obtain the results shown in Figure 8-4. When the head is at rest the rate remains at some fixed value; when the head is rotated in one direction, say clockwise, the rate of firing increases sharply, then declines; when the head is rotated counterclockwise the rate decreases sharply, then comes back to some steady level.

There are also nerve cells in the vestibular nuclei in the medulla that respond differentially to the static orientation of the head, and the activity in

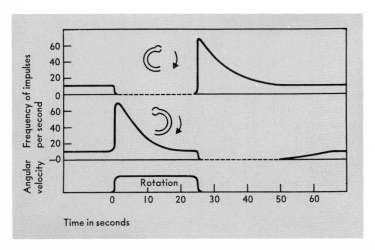

Figure 8-4. The impulse frequency recorded from a single nerve cell from one of the semicircular canals when the head is rotated. (E.D. Adrian. J. Physiol., 1943, 101, 389.)

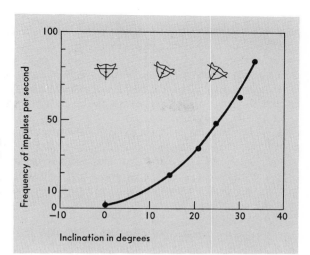

Figure 8-5. The relation between the inclination of the head and the frequency of nerve impulses recorded from single nerve cells from the vestibular system. (E.D. Adrian. J. Physiol., 1943, 101, 389.)

these fibers is probably due to the action of the utricle. The rate of firing in these fibers, measured in terms of impulses per second, is dependent on the inclination of the head with respect to gravitational pull; the greater the angle of inclination from the vertical, the greater the number of impulses per second. An example of the results from one such experiment is shown in Figure 8-5. These fibers from the utricle are found in a part of the vestibular nucleus different from the region where we find fibers from the semicircular canals. There seems to be a spatial localization of the different functions of the vestibular system in the nuclei of the medulla.

The nerve pathways of the vestibular system are not completely known, but they must involve many different regions of the central nervous system. Connections exist between the vestibular system and the cerebellum, a region of the brain that is important in integrating many reflex motor movements involved in coordination and locomotion. Information from the vestibular nuclei is also sent to the centers involved in controlling eye movements. The complete details of the manner in which the vestibular system sends fibers to the higher regions of the brain is not known, but it is known that activity in the vestibular system activates a region of the brain around the lateral, or Sylvian, gyrus.

KINESTHETIC SYSTEM

The kinesthetic sense presents some of the same difficulties encountered in the study of the vestibular system. The basic experimental analyses that are required in order to specify what the sense involves are lacking. Such a comment is not meant to imply that there are no behavioral studies involving these sensory systems; there are many. The problem is to find a large number of studies that involve only, or primarily, the performance of the sense modality we are interested in studying. Experiments that demonstrate

Vestibular
and
Kinesthetic
Senses

how the environment influences the functioning of these senses are extremely difficult to perform. For example, it is not easy to study our ability to detect changes in body position without involving the tactile system.

The early attempts to study the kinesthetic system involved a classic type of experiment in psychophysics, the experiment on lifted weights. Our ability to discriminate differences in the weights of objects was studied in detail in a long chain of experiments done in the early part of the twentieth century. Suppose we offer a subject a reference weight, say 200 grams, and a second weight whose magnitude we vary in the neighborhood of 200 grams, and suppose we ask the subject whether the second weight is greater or less than the reference weight. By systematically varying the value of the second weight we can determine a threshold for detecting weight difference. If we measure the threshold difference in weight, ΔW, that is required by a subject to detect that two weights are different, we find that this threshold difference depends on the reference weight, W. A plot of the ratio, $\Delta W/W$, as a function of the reference weight, W, yields a curve that is very similar to the curves of $\Delta I/I$ obtained from other sense modalities. An example of such a function is shown in Figure 8-6. The difficulty in interpreting these results stems from the fact that such data may result from the blending of sensory input from receptors in the skin when we pick up the weight, from the receptors in the joints as we lift the weight, and from sense cells in muscles involved in lifting the weight.

Experimental studies of skilled movements also involve subtle discriminations of the sensory input from joints and muscles. Our ability to execute responses that deliver given forces, velocities, or accelerations to the experimental apparatus also involve the discrimination of kinesthetic cues.

Much of the experimental work that has been done in psychological laboratories on skilled movements has involved relatively complex responses, such as tracking movements. For example, a subject may be asked to follow a moving target or to keep a metal stylus on a moving line or spot. Such tasks involve what is called eye-hand coordination; part of the feedback the subject receives about his movements is visual. Such visual information is ordinarily

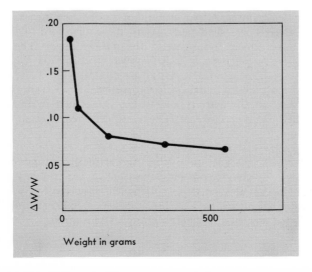

Figure 8-6. Thresholds for the discrimination of differences in weight (expressed as the Weber fraction, $\Delta W/W$) as a function of the magnitude of the reference weight, W. (Modified from R.S. Woodworth and H. Schlosberg. Experimental psychology. New York: Holt, Rinehart and Winston, 1961.)

available in real-life situations, and as a result such studies have considerable practical significance. However, they do not provide us with the basic discrimination data that is required in order to understand how the kinesthetic system works.

A more direct approach to the problem of interest to us is to restrict the movement to a single joint and allow the movement to take place in only one plane. If we do this, the position of the limb can be specified by stating the angle formed at the joint. We can then instruct the subject to place the limb in a given position or to execute a movement of a given extent or at a given speed or acceleration. Subjects can learn to perform under such instructions. Although such performances are somewhat removed from the skilled movements we ordinarily see in human behavior, they provide some of the basic data that are required before we can begin to appreciate how we can sense our bodily movements and positions.

Once again it is difficult to insure that the information utilized by the subject in such a discrimination is coming from a single class of receptors. We know of a number of sense cells that could be operating; we are not sure of the exact role that each type of sense cell plays in this kind of discrimination. Perhaps we can be best guided in our thinking about the behavioral data by turning to the physiological data.

PHYSIOLOGICAL MECHANISMS FOR KINESTHESIS

Besides the tactile system, which we have already discussed, there are at least two other systems that may participate in the kind of discriminations described in the preceding section. The first of these systems is what might loosely be called the muscle sense; the second is referred to as the joint sense. The sensory system most frequently offered as providing the information necessary for fine skilled movements is the muscle sense; it is known to be involved in many reflex movements.

One of the simplest examples of reflex movements is seen in the stretch reflex, the most common instance being the knee jerk. The basic property of the stretch reflex is that when a muscle is stretched it tends to contract reflexly. Sensory equipment located in, or around, muscle fibers is stimulated when we stretch muscle fibers. Impulses are generated in sensory nerves serving muscle tissue, and these fibers send messages to the spinal cord and initiate activity in motor nerve fibers extending to the muscle fibers. The sense cells involved in this reflex pattern are called stretch receptors. If the muscle is stretched, the subsequent contraction of the muscle will, under ordinary circumstances, decrease the stimulation of these stretch receptors, but this contraction will increase the activity of sense cells located in the contractile system itself, the tendon receptors. These sense cells will respond to tension.

These results suggest that we have a delicately balanced machinery to monitor both length and tension. A schematic representation of the arrangement of the structures that are felt to be involved in this dual system is shown in Figure 8-7. It seems certain that this sensory equipment is involved in the reflex components of coordinated movements. It has also been implicated in skilled movements throughout most of the modern study of kinesthesis.

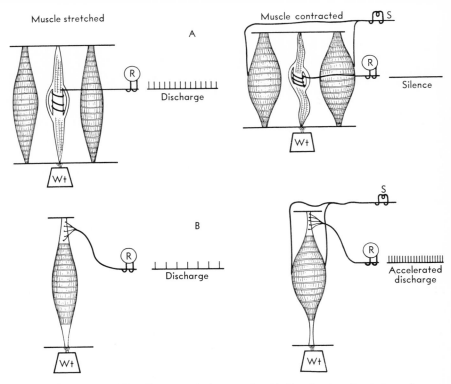

Figure 8-7. The diagram of the muscle spindle showing the types of nerve discharge observed when the muscle is stretched and when it contracts. (H.D. Patton. In T.C. Ruch and J.F. Fulton. Medical physiology and biophysics. Philadelphia: Saunders, 1960.)

Quantitative data have recently been obtained from the joint system which now seems to be a much better candidate for the primary sensory system involved in skilled voluntary movements. Sensory structures located in the joints exhibit a specialization of activity that seems to be ideally suited to monitoring the position of one part of the bony skeleton relative to another part. Individual sensory nerve cells will respond only to a very limited range of positions of a joint. These nerve cells seem to be sharply tuned to a certain range of angles. Such nerve fibers will fire nerve impulses if the joint is at an appropriate angle or passes through an appropriate position. For example, one fiber might respond maximally if the angle made by the forearm and the upper arm is 90°. This nerve fiber would also respond if the elbow angle were 85° or if it were 95°. It will not respond to angles that are more extreme than say 100° or less than 80°. Within the range of 15 or 20 degrees in which it will respond, the rate at which impulses will be generated shows a maximum at some angle, say 90°, and is smaller for angles on either side of 90°. Another fiber might respond maximally at 45° and its effective range might extend from 35° to 55°.

Each of the nerve fibers coming from the joints is specifically tuned to respond to a narrow range of positions, and collectively, these fibers are

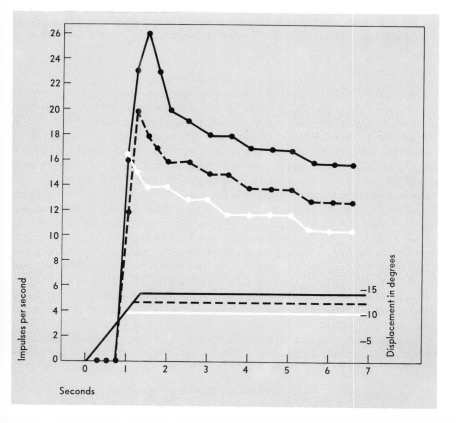

Figure 8-8. The impulse frequency for neurons from the receptors in the knee joint of the cat as a function of the position of the joint (measured in degrees). (After J.E. Rose and V. Mountcastle.)

capable of registering any given position of the limb. An example of this selective sensitivity of a set of such fibers is shown in Figure 8-8. These results are reminiscent of those we encountered in studying the auditory

Figure 8-9. The impulse frequency in knee-joint receptors as a function of time. The three curves represent different amounts of displacement. (In J. Field, H.W. Magoun, and V.E. Hall. Handbook of physiology. Washington, D.C.: American Physiological Society, 1959.)

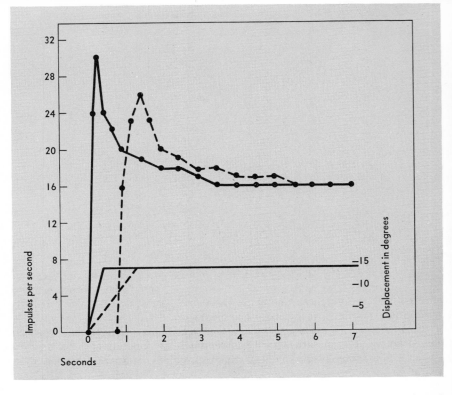

Figure 8-10. The impulse frequency in knee-joint receptors as a function of time. The two curves represent different rates of displacement. (Same source as Figure 8-9.)

system, where each fiber was selectively sensitive to a particular region of the frequency dimension. Such results suggest that we could discriminate the position of the limbs on the basis of which nerve cells are active.

Each nerve fiber in this joint sense will exhibit the phenomenon of adaptation—that is, the fiber will respond more rapidly when the arm is first placed in a position to which the particular nerve fiber is sensitive than it will after the arm has been in that position for some time. An example of this effect is shown in Figures 8-9 and 8-10. This system also has the ability to register the dynamic aspects of limb movement by virtue of the fact that the nerve discharge will be greater if the arm is moved rapidly into a position to which it is sensitive than it will be if moved slowly. However, the final resting rate of nerve discharge will always be the same for a given position of the limb whether the limb was moved to this position rapidly or slowly.

One of the reasons for considering the joint sense in discussing skilled movements is that we know that it is represented in the higher centers of the brain. At the present time there is no substantial evidence that the muscle sense involving the stretch and tension receptors share in this representation.

A Review
of the Properties
# of Sensory Systems

It should be apparent by now that there are many similarities and differences among the various sensory systems, and it might be appropriate to offer a few general comments.

1. All fields of sensory psychology face a common problem that must be solved before we can satisfactorily understand the functioning of a sensory system. The problem is, "What is the appropriate language for describing the stimuli for a given sense modality?" Although scientists have not been equally successful in discovering for the various senses what this language is, progress has been made in all of the senses.

2. In exploring the behavioral phenomena, all fields of sensory psychology share a common methodology, the psychophysical methods. We have not discussed these methods in detail, but we have described some of them in the Introduction.

A number of other psychophysical methods are available to the scientist interested in exploring an organism's response to stimuli. Each has its own advantages and disadvantages. Some of these methods have been omitted deliberately to simplify the treatment and to permit the inclusion of some relevant physiological material. Although the approach to the subject matter of sensory psychology represented by some of these additional methods is different from that represented in this volume, it must be emphasized that the principles of behavioral analysis involved in discussing such methods are, and must be, the same as those employed in understanding the classical methods.

3. A number of general laws seem to apply to all sensory systems, and certain classes of phenomena appear in all sense modalities. For example, all the senses are selectively receptive to environmental changes. One modality may respond to radiant energy whose wavelengths are restricted to one region of the electromagnetic spectrum while another system will respond to another restricted region (for example, the visual system may respond to wavelengths between 400 mμ and 700 mμ, while the temperature system will respond to wavelengths in the infrared region). One system may respond to relatively slow pressure changes (for example, the tactile sense) while another

will respond to very rapid pressure changes (the ear). One sense may be specially sensitive to chemical stimuli in gaseous form, another to chemicals in liquid form. Sometimes the sensitivities may overlap (for example, both the tactile sense and the auditory sense will respond to pressure oscillations in the range from 20 cps to 1000 cps); sometimes the sensitivities do not overlap (for example, the sensitivities of the eye and the joint receptors). Under all circumstances there is a restricted set of environmental changes that will activate each sense system.

All sensory systems seem to operate in a very approximate way on a logarithmic basis. The extent to which this is true provides the empirical foundation for the so-called Weber-Fechner law. This is a rule, attributed to Weber and adopted by Fechner, that our ability to detect threshold differences in intensity depends on the presentation of a fixed fractional, or percentage, increment in intensity. All sense modalities share in showing that this rule holds over some range of stimulus intensity and that it does not hold over the full range of intensities. The deviations from the rule are similar in all sense modalities.

All sensory systems exhibit certain other properties. For example, all show the phenomenon of adaptation, and all show some form of contrast or masking effects.

4. When we compare the various sense modalities, we find the most striking differences in the quantitative details attached to some of the general properties just outlined. Although it is true that both the tactile and auditory systems are responsive to pressure changes, there are striking differences in the absolute sensitivities to pressure and the range of frequencies over which the system will respond. Although all senses show approximately the same variations in the difference thresholds as we change the magnitude of the comparison stimulus, the numerical value of the difference thresholds differs systematically from one modality to another. Similar statements can be made about the phenomenon of adaptation: Although all sense modalities display this effect, the quantitative details vary greatly from one modality to another.

5. Neither the similarities nor the differences should be considered to be surprising or trivial. On the basis of what we have seen of the mechanisms that are involved in each modality we should expect these results. Each sensory system has its own transducing mechanism, its mechanism for transforming environmental energy changes into changes inside the organism that are physiologically useful. The eye does this with a very sensitive, complex photochemical system; the ear does this with a complex mechanical system that resonates to certain frequencies and that adjusts for the fact that it responds to forces in air and must convert these to forces in liquid. The physical characteristics of these resonances, of this impedance matching, of the damping characteristics of the middle and inner ear—all of these features of the auditory system leave their mark on the behavioral and physiological data we obtain.

After the impact of these various transducing mechanisms has been registered, it must be the case that all sensory systems share in having to transmit any information they receive through nerve tissue. The properties of nerve conduction, of synaptic transmission, of excitatory and inhibitory effects in the nervous system, all leave their stamp on the data we obtain, and these properties may be expected to be the same in all sense modalities. For example, there are many similarities between the receptive fields of single nerve fibers in the visual system expressed in terms of visual angle and the receptive fields of tactile nerve fibers expressed in terms of the region of the skin stimulated. The complexities of "on-off" responding is also characteristic of all sensory fibers in the central nervous system.

6. We cannot, and should not, expect that there will be obvious short-cuts to the understanding of how our sensory systems work. It is difficult to describe adequately what we see and hear without acquiring some understanding of the physics of the environment to which we respond. This does not mean that all of us must become physicists; it does mean that we must adopt a scholarly attitude about the sciences with which we must interact. Only detailed procedures and experiments, dictated by the sensory results already available and involving a sophisticated understanding of the specific areas of the physical and biological sciences that are necessarily implicated, can possibly yield the kinds of results now needed in order to provide us with new insights about how we perceive the world around us. Only an understanding of the sciences involved in such experiments will allow us to appreciate the importance of such experiments when they are reported. We must be prepared, on the one hand, to abandon any shibboleths that may now direct the way we think about problems in sensory psychology; we must, on the other hand, maintain a perspective with respect to attractive new theories that seem to offer interesting solutions to one or more existing problems without offering any sensible statement about the large set of problems we now seem to understand with our present theoretical framework. It may be tempting, for example, to accept the suggestion of a two-component theory of color vision on the basis of a number of recent interesting and thought-provoking demonstrations. It would not be sensible to do so without first asking how such a notion could handle, in an explicit and quantitative manner, the work of the past 100 years on such specific issues as visibility, color mixing, wavelength discrimination, color blindness, and many other topics.

The past decade has provided the impetus for many substantial changes in our thinking about the fields of sensory psychology. Some of these advances have been based primarily on behavioral data, some have been based primarily on the physiological data, but in all cases they represent some form of interaction between the two. For example, our views of color vision and adaptation in vision and our views of pitch perception in audition have been remarkably enhanced in the past ten years. No one of these changes in viewpoint, however, has been achieved without a contribution from both physiological and behavioral research. Each line of activity gains strength from the other.

It is likely that the next ten years will see major advances occurring in our understanding of complex sensory phenomena, phenomena that are frequently put under the rubric of perception. We have tried to emphasize in the chapter on vision that the problems here are not different in kind; they are, however, different in complexity. Recent experiments have begun to unfold some of the physiological mechanisms involved in form perception, perception of speed or direction of movement, and so on. What is now required in these areas is the kind of collaborative effort that has characterized the study of such problems as adaptation and visibility, that is, an interaction of research interests and experimental designs between those doing behavioral, and those doing physiological experiments.

Selected Readings

Boring, E.G. *Sensation and perception in the history of experimental psychology.* New York: Appleton-Century Co., Inc., 1942.

Geldard, F.A. *The human senses.* New York: Wiley, 1953.

Hirsh, I. *The measurement of hearing.* New York: McGraw-Hill, 1952.

LeGrand, Y. *Light, colour, and vision.* London: Chapman and Hall, Ltd., 1957.

Moncrief, R.W. *The chemical senses.* New York: Wiley, 1946.

Morgan, C.T. *Physiological psychology* (Third ed.). New York: McGraw-Hill, 1952.

Osgood, C.E. *Method and theory in experimental psychology.* New York: Oxford University Press, 1953.

Stevens, S.S. (ed.). *Handbook of experimental psychology.* New York: Wiley, 1951.

Woodworth, R.S., and H. Schlosberg. *Experimental psychology* (Revised ed.). New York: Holt, Rinehart and Winston, 1961.

Index